DIGITAL
COMPUTER
FUNDAMENTALS

PRENTICE-HALL SERIES IN ELECTRONIC TECHNOLOGY

IRVING L. KOSOW, editor

CHARLES M. THOMSON and JOSEPH J. GERSHON, consulting editors

PRENTICE-HALL INTERNATIONAL, INC., *London*
PRENTICE-HALL OF AUSTRALIA, PTY., LTD., *Sydney*
PRENTICE-HALL OF CANADA, LTD., *Toronto*
PRENTICE-HALL OF INDIA (PRIVATE) LTD., *New Dehli*
PRENTICE-HALL OF JAPAN, INC., *Tokyo*

DIGITAL
COMPUTER
FUNDAMENTALS

Litton Industries, inc., Beverly Hills, California
Data Systems Division
Technical Training Group

PRENTICE-HALL, INC.,
Englewood Cliffs, N.J.

Library of Congress Catalog Card Number 65-21177

Printed in the United States of America
21429C
21427C

0   1318138

INITIAL COUNT

As the reader will learn, the number zero and the count zero are very important in the digital world. I feel that a chapter with the number 0 must likewise be important to this text.

In the course of conducting classes on digital computers for military engineers and technicians, Litton instructors found that no single textbook told simply what digital computers are made of, how they are put together, and what they do.

In early 1960, the Technical Training Group of Data Systems Division of Litton Industries began to assemble this kind of information; they later used the published version under the title "Digital Computer Fundamentals."

This book, the refined and expanded "Digital Computer Fundamentals," was written for the person who, having an average technical background in analog circuit electronics, needs to build a similar competence in the digital field. To some extent this book treats every aspect of digital computers; however, some chapters of the book cover subjects that are given over to entire graduate-level textbooks. If after reading these pages, the reader feels further study is needed on a subject, he will find ample published material listed in the bibliography. I have found by repeated classroom use of this text that the material it contains is sufficient to bring a person confidently "on board" in the digital field.

The circuit examples and typical design values used throughout the text are similar to those used in digital equipment presently being manufactured within the defense industry. In fact, many sample circuits are merely simplified versions of circuits used in the digital equipment that Litton manufactures.

Little of the material in this book is original with the authors. The text is, after all, an exposition of principles and circuits that are used, that work. At the same time, the treatment of the material is new and the circuits and functions discussed are current. For example, the material is arranged in a way that progressively helps the reader to understand subsequent material; moreover, many subjects, like the integrated circuits of Chapter 4, are covered in a novel and easy-to-understand manner.

I would like to thank the many people who were involved in the preparation of this text, and particularly to acknowledge the contributions of Mr. Roland L. Bassett, Mr. Edward F. Fenn, and Mr. Keith McClung of the Technical Training Staff; to thank Mr. Donald Powell and Miss Vera Freund, who edited the manuscripts and gave valuable suggestions; and finally, to sympathize with the artists in the Technical Illustration Group whose job it was to decipher my sketches.

MILAN G. MOODY

Van Nuys, California

CONTENTS

*DIGITAL
COMPUTER
FUNDAMENTALS*

1

INTRODUCTION

1-1 Computer History

The development of computer technology stands as one of the greatest achievements of modern man. Computers have advanced the frontiers of science by solving problems that men, unassisted by machines, could not complete within several lifetimes. Computers have saved mankind countless hours and dollars in many fields, particularly in business and science.

The evolution of computers began with man's earliest efforts to extend his intelligence into new fields. In doing so, he became increasingly aware of his limitations in speed and capacity to perform the many mathematical operations attendant upon almost any scientific endeavor. One of the earliest attempts to remedy this lack resulted in the abacus, still useful in some applications even today. Early in the nineteenth century an Englishman named Babbage invented a mechanical device that he called a "difference engine." Although the "difference engine" could only perform repetitive subtractions, it could probably be called the first "fixed-program" computer. Crude though it was, Babbage's device marked the beginning of man's efforts to reduce the drudgery of repetitive arithmetic operations. From this early start the mechanical

1

adding machines and calculators of today have evolved. The mechanical calculators were only a partial solution to the problem, for even the most modern of these still require man, limited by his relatively slow thinking and reaction speeds, as an integral part of their operation. Modern computers, on the other hand, are capable of progressing through a preplanned routine to the complete solution of a problem at their own speed and are thus inherently faster, limited only by their mechanical and electrical response times.

There are two basic categories into which all true computers are grouped: *analog* computers and *digital* computers. Analog computers utilize voltages, shaft positions, rate of change, or some other analog of a discrete quantity. For example, if an analog computer were to add 2+4, the computer might use 5 volts to represent 2, and 10 volts to represent 4, and would then "sum" 5 and 10 volts in a summing amplifier. This technique of computing is easy to mechanize, but if two very precise numbers, such as 2.000+4.000, were to be added, then the voltages representing these numbers would also have to be very accurate — and it is difficult to maintain extremely precise voltages for any length of time. Digital computers are mechanized to use actual numbering systems. That is, they use two-state logic, either "on" or "off," to represent the presence or absence of a number. Because of this basic feature of utilizing the two extremes of a condition, digital computers are inherently more accurate than analog computers. However, analog computers are more appropriate to, for instance, simple problem solution than are digital computers, which require, even for the simplest problem, that any values used be changed to digital quantities, and which usually will not be smaller than an established minimum size. Hence, it proves expensive to use a digital computer to solve very simple problems. In general, however, recent design favors digital computation, since it is the most direct approach to the basic problem of simplifying and reducing the work load in repetitive mathematical operations. Digital computation also possesses a faster program capability than analog computation because switching between two extremes is inherently faster than ranging gradually over a multitude of possible values.

Computers are divided not only into digital and analog categories, but also into two other categories — *general-purpose* (GP) and *special-purpose* (SP).

General-purpose computers can solve a variety of problems; they can be made to perform, at different times, any of the series of additions, subtractions, multiplications, and divisions required by any mathematical problem. Each problem to be solved will require its own set of instructions for correctly sequencing the required mathematical operations. The process of writing these instructions is called *programming*.

Special-purpose computers usually require less hardware to solve a problem than do general-purpose computers. However, special-purpose computers are limited to solving only one specific problem. For example, it is possible to construct a computer that will solve for the sine of any angle. Since the sine of an angle equals the opposite side of a triangle divided by the hypotenuse, the value of the opposite side and the value of the hypotenuse can be fed into circuits that would always cause this division to occur to produce the solution. Such a computer could solve for the sine of *any* angle but *only* for the sine of an angle. Since it cannot be used for any other purpose, it is called a special-purpose computer.

There is a tendency to become overwhelmed by the speed and accuracy of these machines. However, it should be remembered that computers do not reason. They only perform time-consuming, repetitive operations. Humans do the reasoning for them when they select the programs.

All digital computers contain the following basic elements (units):

- Input Unit
- Output Unit
- Memory or Storage Unit
- Arithmetic Unit
- Control and Timing Unit
- Program Unit

These basic units are illustrated in Fig. 1–1.

1–2 Input-Output Unit

The world is analog in nature in that things exist in quantities. Quantities may be represented by numbers. Inputs to computers may be from many sources (radar signals, radio signals, tapes, etc.), almost all analog (quantitative) in nature. The input unit is necessary to assign digital values to these analog quantities (so the computer can manipulate them). After the computer solves a problem, it is necessary to convert the solution for some display or readout device. Usually these display devices are analog in nature, so the digital information is then reconverted to analog information. This conversion is controlled by the output unit.

1-3 Memory Unit

The computer must be capable of storing facts or data to be used in later calculations. These data are held in a storage or memory unit. The technique used to store this information varies, and the more common forms of storage will be discussed later. Placing information into storage (the memory) is called *writing*, and sensing what has already been stored is called *reading*. The memory unit allows a digital computer to remember problems or facts for an indefinite period of time, much like the human brain, but without the human brain's memory loss.

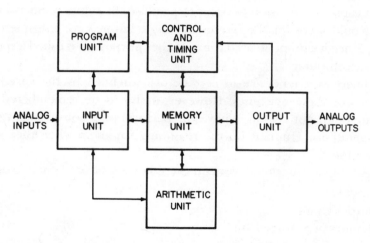

Fig. 1-1. Digital computer basic elements.

1-4 Arithmetic Unit

Since the function of a computer is to solve problems, an arithmetic unit is needed. This unit is normally mechanized so that it will add, subtract, multiply, divide, and perform square root and other operations. All actual computations take place in this unit.

1-5 Control and Timing Unit

It is obvious that some method of control must exist. As mentioned before, assume an arithmetic unit that can add, subtract and perform other operations. When should it add? When subtract? Control signals that can, for example, "enable" the add circuitry and "disable" the other circuitry at the correct time are produced by the control and timing unit. Timing is also necessary to allow input information to be received at the

correct time and in proper sequence, step it through the prescribed
program, and then produce an output.

1-6 Program Unit

A computer is designed to perform a certain number of distinct
operations such as addition, subtraction, and the transfer of numbers
from one place to another. These operations are usually called *instructions*. The number of instructions a computer can perform is determined
by its original design. To solve a complex problem, it is frequently
necessary to manipulate numbers, by various instructions, in a certain
prescribed sequence. When this sequence is determined, it is called the
program, and the person who determines it is the *programmer*.

Thus, a programmer determines the sequence of steps necessary to
solve a problem within the design capabilities of a computer. This
sequence is placed in the program unit. The program unit (through the
action of the control and timing unit) causes inputs to be accepted
(through the input unit), the problem to be manipulated (through an
interaction of the memory unit and the arithmetic unit), and the answer
to be displayed (through the output unit).

The previous illustrations have purposely been kept simple. Usually
the circuits of these units are time-shared and overlapped in a complex
manner. With the exception of the memory unit, it is usually impossible
to find a given drawer or space that is set aside for one of the particular
units. Most units are dispersed throughout the computer to reduce
wiring and to increase efficiency.

1-7 Text Organization

The textbook material that follows will first cover the fundamentals
needed to explore each of the digital computer units and will then cover
each unit in a separate chapter. The material will be summarized by
using the knowledge gained through studying each chapter to design a
sample general-purpose computer.

2

BINARY NUMBERS

2-1 Introduction

During the course of history it became necessary to "count," or represent by symbols, the quantity of "things." The Romans used clumsy symbols (Roman numerals) and hence lost out to the more versatile Arabic symbols, which have become practically universal. But not only did the world make a choice of symbols, but also a choice of how many symbols would be used; hence, we have evolved with the decimal, or base-ten, numbering system. That is, ten distinct characters (0, 1, 2, 3, 4, 5, 6, 7, 8, 9) were chosen, no doubt because there are a total of ten fingers and thumbs. All the arithmetic processes performed (addition, subtraction, multiplication, etc.); all the measurements made (inches, kilometers, miles, etc.); all the breakdowns of money (dimes, quarters, dollars, etc.) are done with ten symbols—the decimal system. However, the choice could have been for more than ten symbols to form a numbering system, or it could have been for less. In fact, many numbering (or counting) systems other than the decimal system are used today, and all are based on the same rules that apply to the decimal system. These other numbering systems are often better suited for particular applications.

6

2-2 Numbering Systems

The decimal numbering system contains *ten* basic characters.

0, 1, 2, 3, 4, 5, 6, 7, 8, 9

Using the same symbols, the noval system contains *nine* characters.

0, 1, 2, 3, 4, 5, 6, 7, 8

The octal system contains *eight* characters.

0, 1, 2, 3, 4, 5, 6, 7

The septary system contains *seven* characters.

0, 1, 2, 3, 4, 5, 6

The quinary system contains *five* characters.

0, 1, 2, 3, 4

The quatary system contains *four* characters.

0, 1, 2, 3

The trinary system contains *three* characters.

0, 1, 2

The binary system contains *two* characters.

0, 1

Numbering systems greater than decimal would need some new symbols. For instance:

The unodecimal system contains *eleven* characters.

0, 1, 2, 3, 4, 5, 6, 7, 8, 9, a

The duodecimal system contains *twelve* characters.

0, 1, 2, 3, 4, 5, 6, 7, 8, 9, a, b

Eleven "things" would be represented decimally by 11 (eleven) but duodecimally by b, hence, 11 in the decimal equals b in the duodecimal.

Notice that each system has as many distinct characters as the name of the system implies, hence each system is "in the base" that the name implies. That is, decimal system—ten characters—base ten; octal system—eight characters—base eight; binary system—two characters—base two; etc. The base (often called *radix*) is numerically one greater than the value of the largest character, or symbol, of the system. Among these numbering systems, the decimal, octal, and binary find the most use in digital devices. To understand the interchangeable capabilities of these numbering systems, we must examine the rules of the decimal system and the process of changing from one radix to another. Notice carefully that no system has a character as great as its radix. Maximum character = radix − 1.

2-3 The Decimal System

Since we use relatively few "characters" to represent relatively large "numbers" (quantities of "things"), it is evident that the value of a particular digit depends not only on the character itself but on the "order" or position of the character. For instance, the decimal number 456 has only three characters and yet it represents four hundred and fifty-six "things." Obviously, the 5 has more "power," or is in a higher "order" than the 6, yet the symbol 5 is less than the symbol 6, likewise the 4 has a higher order than either the 5 or 6 and yet its symbolic value is less than either 5 or 6. In fact, the number 456 is $400 + 50 + 6 = 456$. The 6 is in the "units" position, the 5 is in the "tens" position, and the 4 is in the "hundreds" position. This is the same as saying the 6 is a first-order number, the 5 is a second-order number, and 4 is a third-order number. For another example, examine the number 3782. This is:

$$3000 + 700 + 80 + 2 = 3782$$

This number may also be expressed as a series.

$$(3 \times 10^3) + (7 \times 10^2) + (8 \times 10^1) + (2 \times 10^0)$$
$$= (3 \times 1000) + (7 \times 100) + (8 \times 10) + (2 \times 1)$$
$$= 3000 + 700 + 80 + 2 = 3782$$

The radix (10) is raised to the power corresponding to the order and multiplied by character at the corresponding order (any number raised to the zero power is, by definition, equal to "one").

The digit to the right, representing the smallest quantity, is known as the *least significant digit* (LSD) and the far left digit the *most significant digit* (MSD).

Fractional numbers may be expanded similarly. The decimal

$$1 \times 10^{-1} + 7 \times 10^{-2} + 1 \times 10^{-3} + 3 \times 10^{-4}$$
$$= (1 \times 0.1) + (7 \times 0.01) + (1 \times 0.001) + (3 \times 0.0001)$$
$$= \frac{1}{10} + \frac{7}{100} + \frac{1}{1000} + \frac{3}{10,000} = 0 \cdot 1713$$

Any number in any system (any base) may be expanded in this same type of power series.

2-4 Conversion of Radix

By using the power series, we can express any number (with a base equal to, or less than, ten) as a *decimal* number. For instance, the decimal number 302 is expanded to:

$$3\times10^2 + 0\times10^1 + 2\times10^0$$

$$= 3\times100 + 2\times10 + 2\times1$$

$$= 302_{10} \qquad \text{(subscript indicates radix)}$$

The octal number 456_8 expands to:

$$(4\times8^2) + (5\times8^1) + (6\times8^0)$$

$$= (4\times64) + (5\times8) + (6\times1)$$

$$= 256 + 40 + 6 = 302_{10}$$

The binary number 100101110_2 expands to:

$$(1\times2^8) + (0\times2^7) + (0\times2^6) + (1\times2^5) + (0\times2^4) + (1\times2^3) + (1\times2^2)$$

$$+ (1\times2^1) + (0\times2^0)$$

$$= (1\times256) + (0\times128) + (0\times64) + (1\times32) + (0\times16) + (1\times8) + (1\times4)$$

$$+ (1\times2) + (0\times1)$$

$$= 256 + 0 + 0 + 32 + 0 + 8 + 4 + 2 + 0 = 302_{10}$$

Then:

$$302_{10} = 456_8 = 100101110_2$$

This must be read "three hundred two" equals "four-five-six, base eight" equals "one-zero-zero-one-zero-one-one-one-zero, base two." 456_8 is not equal to "four hundred fifty six." When a number in any base (10 or less) is expanded by the power series it yields a base-10 number because the expansion process is done by "decimal arithmetic." For instance, the expansion of 456_8 was:

$$4\times8^2 = (4\times8\times8) = 256$$

$$+ 5\times8^1 = (5\times8) \quad = \quad 40 \qquad \text{These are all regular}$$

$$+ 6\times8^0 = (6\times1) \quad = \quad 6 \qquad \text{"decimal" operations}$$

RULE 1: To convert a given number, in a smaller radix, to its equivalent number in radix ten expand by:

$$\ldots + AR^4 + AR^3 + AR^2 + AR^1 + AR^0 + AR^{-1} + AR^{-2} + \ldots$$

where coefficient A represents the characters in their given order and R represents the radix of the number being converted.

EXAMPLE

$1011.11_2 = ?_{10}$

Expand:

$$1 \times 2^3 + 0 \times 2^2 + 1 \times 2^1 + 1 \times 2^0 + 1 \times 2^{-1} + 1 \times 2^{-2}$$
$$= 1 \times 8 + 0 \times 4 + 1 \times 2 + 1 \times 1 + 1 \times 0.5 + 1 \times 0.25$$
$$= 8 + 0 + 2 + 1 + 0.5 + 0.25 = 11.75_{10}$$

(Remember, any number raised to a negative power may be expressed as a reciprocal, hence $2^{-1} = 1/2^1 = 0.5$.)

When it is desired to convert from the *base 10* to a smaller base the same process of expansion applies but with greater difficulty. If 173_{10} is given and it is desired to convert this decimal number to the base-eight number (octal), there is certainly an expansion in the powers of eight that equals 173_{10}.

Lay out a tentative expansion (in base eight),

$$? \times 8^3 + ? \times 8^2 + ? \times 8^1 + ? \times 8^0 = 173_{10}$$

and remove the biggest "piece" of 173_{10} possible.

Eight cubed equals 512_{10}, which is greater than 173, hence this term may be crossed out. Eight squared equals 64_{10} and this is less than 173_{10}; therefore, this term may be used. The next step will be to determine the coefficient for this term. If seven is used (the maximum possible coefficient), the value of this term would be $7 \times 64 = 448$, which is greater than 173. $2 \times 64 = 128$, which is the closest value to 173 obtainable from this term. $173 - 128 = 45$, which is what now remains of 173 and must be taken care of in the 8^1 and 8^0 terms. 8^1 equals 8 (which is less than 45), and the maximum usable coefficient would be 5.

Five times eight is forty, and forty from forty-five leaves 5 to be taken care of in the 8^0 term. 8^0 equals 1 and $5 \times 1 = 5$, which takes care of the "5" remainder. The expansion then appears as:

$2 \times 8^2 + 5 \times 8^1 + 5 \times 8^0$ (using the previously determined coefficients)

$$2 \times 8^2 = 128$$
$$+ 5 \times 8^1 = 40$$
$$\underline{+ 5 \times 8^0 = 5}$$
$$= 173_{10}$$

The octal number that equals 173_{10} is 255_8.

EXAMPLE:

Convert decimal 73 to a binary number.

$$?\times2^7 + ?\times2^6 + ?\times2^5 + ?\times2^4 + ?\times2^3 + ?\times2^2 + ?\times2^1 + ?\times2^0$$

$2^7 = 128_{10}$ (greater than 73, cross out)

$2^6 = 64_{10}$ (OK, less than 73)

$73 - 64 = 9$ remainder

$2^4 = 16$ (greater than 9, cross out)

$2^3 = 8$ (OK, less than 9)

$9 - 8 = 1$ remainder

$2^2 = 4$ (greater than 1, cross out)

$2^1 = 2$ (greater than 1, cross out)

$2^0 = 1$ (OK, equal to 1)

Expansion:

$$1\times2^6 + 0\times2^5 + 0\times2^4 + 1\times2^3 + 0\times2^2 + 0\times2^1 + 1\times2^0 = 73_{10}$$

Then the binary number is:

$$1001001_2 = 73_{10}$$

This same expansion process will convert a base-ten decimal fraction to a smaller base. For example:

Convert 0.625_{10} to binary equivalent.

$$0.?\times2^{-1} + ?\times2^{-2} + ?\times2^{-3} + ?\times2^{-4} + \ldots$$

$2^{-1} = 0.5$ (OK, less than 0.625)

$0.625 - 0.5 = 0.125$ remainder

$2^{-2} = 0.25$ (greater than 0.125, cross out)

$2^{-3} = 0.125$ (OK, equals 0.125)

Expansion:

$$0.1\times2^{-1} + 0\times2^{-2} + 1\times2^{-3} = 0.625_{10}$$

Then the binary fraction is $0.101_2 = 0.625_{10}$

A more straightforward way of converting from the *base 10* to a smaller base is to *divide* the given decimal number by the desired radix as many times as possible, noting the remainders (this works for *whole* numbers only). For instance:

Convert whole number 173_{10} to an octal number.

$\dfrac{21}{8)\,173}$ +5 remainder (LSD of octal answer)

$\dfrac{2}{8)\ 21}$ +5 remainder

$\dfrac{0}{8)\ \ 2}$ +2 remainder (MSD of octal answer)

Then

$$173_{10} = 255_8$$

Check:

$$2 \times 8^2 + 5 \times 8^1 + 5 \times 8^0 = 173_{10}$$

EXAMPLE:

$$73_{10} = ?_2.$$

$\dfrac{36}{2)\,73}$ +1 remainder (LSD)

$\dfrac{18}{2)\,36}$ +0 remainder

$\dfrac{9}{2)\,18}$ +0 remainder

$\dfrac{4}{2)\ \,9}$ +1 remainder

$\dfrac{2}{2)\ \,4}$ +0 remainder

$\dfrac{1}{2)\ \,2}$ +0 remainder

$\dfrac{0}{2)\ \,1}$ +1 remainder (MSD)

Then

$$1001001_2 = 73_{10}$$

A similar straightforward technique may be applied when converting decimal fractions to fractions in a smaller base. To do this *multiply* the given decimal fraction by the desired base and note the values that "overflow" into whole numbers. For instance:

Convert 0.4375_{10} to an octal fraction.

$$0.4375$$
$$\times 8$$

(MSD) 3 overflow   3.5000

0.5000
8

(LSD) 4 overflow   4.0000

0.0000
8

No overflow   0.0000

Therefore, the octal fraction is 0.34_8.

Check:

$$3\times8^{-1}+4\times8^{-2}=3\times0.125+4\times0.015615=0.4375_{10}$$

EXAMPLE:

Convert 0.7813_{10} to a binary fraction

0.7813
2

(MSD) 1   1.5626

0.5626
2

1   1.1252

0.1252
2

0   0.2504

0.2504
2

0   0.5008

0.5008
2

(LSD) 1   1.0016

0.0016 is small enough to neglect. Then the binary fraction is 0.011001.

As can be seen, it is not always possible to convert evenly a decimal fraction to some smaller-base equivalent, but a close approximation can be made within a few places, and if the fraction is not a repeating type, an exact equivalent can be realized if the process is carried out far enough.

RULE 2a: To convert a whole number from radix 10 to a smaller radix:

(a) Divide the given number by the new radix, noting the remainders, continuously, until the quotient is zero.

(b) Arrange the remainders with the first as the LSD and the last as the ᴹ̃ SD.

RULE 2b: To convert a fractional number from radix 10 to a smaller fractional radix:

(a) Multiply by the new radix, noting the overflows, continuously, until the product is zero.

(b) Arrange the overflows with the first as the MSD and the last as the LSD.

Notice that the previous conversion examples always pass from the base 10 to some new base or from some given base to the base 10. If it is desired to change from, say, the base 7 to the base 3, the most straightforward way would be to convert the base 7 to base 10, then to base 3.

These conversion techniques indicate that there is an equivalent relationship between different numbering systems. For instance, the decimal number 531_{10} has an equivalent octal number 1023_8, and an equivalent binary number 1000010011_2, and vice versa. This is an important consideration because the design of an electrical circuit to mechanize (into a computer) the decimal system would necessitate a circuit that could differentiate between ten states, or ten levels, to represent the values of the ten decimal symbols. This is not impossible, but a circuit that simply needs to differentiate between two states (as with binary numbers) will be far less complex. In the binary system, only two states, or levels, would be necessary to represent all the binary characters and this could be accomplished with a switch. Switch-on could represent a one, and switch-off could represent a zero. This same effect could be accomplished with a relay (energized or de-energized), a tube (saturated or cut off), etc. By conversion techniques, normal decimal numbers can be changed to binary numbers and handled easily by electronic switching circuits.

2–5 Arithmetic Operations with Binary Numbers

For a computer to be versatile, it must be able to perform any arithmetic computation and, since the computer will be mechanized to handle binary numbers, it must be able to perform these computations in a binary fashion. It is essential to learn these methods of computation to design or check a digital computer.

A. BINARY ADDITION

All the possible combinations of two binary numbers being added are considered below:

Binary Number		Decimal Number			Binary Number		Decimal Number
0	=	0	Augend		1	=	1
+0	=	+0	Addend		+1	=	+1
0	=	0	Sum		10	=	2
					carry		

0	=	0	Augend
+1	=	+1	Addend
1	=	1	Sum

Binary addition is simple enough until the combination of binary $1 + 1$ is encountered. In decimal $1 + 1 = 2$, but the binary equivalent of decimal 2 is 10 (one-zero), and, therefore, when two binary one's are to be added, a carry is propagated into the second-order column producing a sum:

$$10 \text{ (one-zero)} = 1 \times 2^1 + 0 \times 2^0$$
$$= (1 \times 2) + (0 \times 1) = 2_{10}$$

Further examples:

ADD:

Carry	1111	
Augend	10110101	$= 181_{10}$
Addend	11011010	$= 218_{10}$
	110001111	$= 399_{10}$

ADD:

Carry	111	
Augend	11011	$= 27$
	111100	$= 60$
	1010111	$= 87$

B. BINARY SUBTRACTION

All possible combinations of the two binary numbers being subtracted are considered below:

Binary Number	Decimal Number		Binary Number	Decimal Number
0	0	Minuend	1	1
−0	−0	Subtrahend	−1	−1
0	0	Remainder	0	0
1	1	Minuend	0	0
−0	−0	Subtrahend	−1	−1
1	1	Remainder	X	X

X = CANNOT BE
DONE WITHOUT
BORROWING

Binary subtraction is straightforward until the combination $0 - 1$ is encountered. As with decimal numbers, no subtraction can be performed unless the minuend is equal to, or greater than, the subtrahend (in arithmetic, but not in algebra). The following values illustrate the process of "borrowing."

	Binary Number		Decimal Number
Minuend	1 ^{1}0	=	2
Sutrahend	−·1		−·1
Remainder	0 1	=	1

The binary "one" in the second column is "borrowed from" and moved over to the first column. In the process of removing this one the second column becomes a zero and the first column becomes 10 (not ten, but "one-zero" which is equal to "two"). "One" from "one-zero" equals "one" (1 from 2 equals 1). As a further example, consider the values given below.

$$100 = 4$$
$$\underline{-1 = 1}$$
$$011 = 3 \qquad (1 \times 2^1) + (1 \times 2^0) = 3_{10}$$

$$0 \quad 1 \quad 1_0$$

3rd 2nd 1st

Columns

EXAMPLES:

$$100110 = 38$$
$$\underline{-11010 = 26}$$
$$001100 = 12$$

$$100010011 = 275$$
$$\underline{-111111 = 63}$$
$$11010100 - 212$$

C. SUBTRACTION BY COMPLEMENTING

The subtraction operation is accomplished in most computers by an addition process. To perform subtraction by addition, it is necessary to complement the subtrahend. Subtraction by addition (complementing method) will first be examined in decimal numbers. For example, subtract 32 from 54. The first step is to complement the subtrahend, 32. Since the decimal system is based on the "powers of ten," the complement of a number, say 6, is the difference between 6 and the next higher power of ten. Six is of the 10^0 order; hence, the next higher power of ten is $10^1 = 10$.

$$10 - 6 = 4 \qquad (\text{4 is the complement of 6})$$

$$100 - 32 = 68 \qquad (\text{68 is the complement of 32})$$

$$1000 - 263 = 737 \quad (\text{737 is the complement of 263})$$

Therefore:

$$\begin{array}{ccc} 54 & & 54 \\ \underline{-32} & \text{or} & \underline{+68} \quad (\text{complement of 32}) \\ 22 & & ①22 \end{array}$$

carry

A carry always occurs in the highest-order column (in this case the third column) when subtraction by addition is performed, but it may be disregarded since it is *known* that a "remainder answer" is desired and a remainder answer cannot possibly be as large as, or larger than, either of the operators (minuend and subtrahend). As a further example, subtract 3 from 9 by complementing the subtrahend.

$$\begin{array}{cc} 10 & 9 \\ \underline{-3} & \underline{+7} \\ \text{7 (complement of 3)} & ①6 \quad \text{answer} = 6 \end{array}$$

carry (drop)

It must be realized that, so far, the examples have dealt with operators of the *same* order (54 is the same order as 32, 9 is the same order as 3). If the orders of the operators are different, and subtraction by complementing is to be performed, the complement of the subtrahend is obtained by subtracting it from the power of ten that is one order *higher* than the *highest* order operator (which will be the minuend). That is, should it be required to subtract 8 from 132 by complementing, then the complement of 8 for this problem would be:

$$1000 \qquad\qquad\qquad 132$$
$$\underline{-\ 8} \qquad\qquad\qquad \underline{+992}$$
$$992 \quad \text{(complement of 8)} \qquad ①124 \quad \text{answer} = 124$$
$$\text{carry (drop)}$$

This form of complementing is loosely known as the "ten's complement"-method. A "nine's complement" provides a more practical method of subtracting by addition; thus the complement is obtained by subtracting from 9 or 99 or 999, etc., rather than from 10 or 100 or 1000, etc., which always requires borrowing. The complement of a number such as 32 is obtained by subtracting 32 from 99 instead of from 100.

$$99 \qquad\qquad\qquad\qquad 100$$
$$\underline{-32} \qquad\qquad\qquad\qquad \underline{-\ 32}$$
$$67 \quad \text{(nine's complement)} \qquad 68 \quad \text{(ten's complement)}$$

Notice that the addition of a "one" to the nine's complement would yield the ten's complement. If 32 were subtracted from 54 using the nine's complement it would appear as:

$$54$$
$$\underline{+67} \quad \text{(nine's complement of 32)}$$
$$\text{carry} \rightarrow ①21$$
$$\hookrightarrow 1$$
$$\overline{22}$$

When using the nine's complement, the carry is brought down and added to the LSD of the first answer (21), yielding the correct answer, 22. The technique of using the carry is termed as "end-around-carry."

EXAMPLE:
Subtract 3 from 7 by the nine's-complement method.

$$9 \qquad\qquad\qquad\qquad 7$$
$$\underline{-3} \qquad\qquad\qquad\qquad \underline{+6}$$
$$6 \quad \text{(nine's complement of 3)} \qquad ①3$$
$$\hookrightarrow 1$$
$$\overline{\quad}$$
$$4 \text{ correct answer}$$

The subtraction of binary numbers by complementing and adding is accomplished in much the same manner. The complement of 110, for example, is obtained by subtracting 110 from the next higher power of two. Since 110 is a third-order number, the next higher order is a fourth order, or $2^3 = 1000$. Suppose 110 is to be subtracted from 111 by the complementing method.

```
 1000                              111
−  110                           +010
 0010   (two's complement of 110)   ①001   answer = 001
                                    carry (drop)
```

EXAMPLES:

Subtract 1110 from 100100 by complementing. The two's complement of 1110 must be obtained from a power of two, one order higher than the minuend, 100100.

```
 1000000                          100100
−    1110                        +110010
  110010   (two's complement of 1110)   ①010110   answer = 010110
                                        carry (drop)
```

As with decimal numbers, it is easier to obtain a binary complement if the "one's complement" is used instead of the "two's complement" (just as the nine's complement was easier to use than the ten's complement). Both types of complements for 110 are compared below.

```
 1000                          111   one less than 1000
−  110                        − 110
 0010   (two's complement)     001   (one's complement)
```

EXAMPLE:

Subtract 110 from 111 using the one's complement.

```
 111                              111
−110                            + 001
 001   (one's complement)        ①000
                                    ↳1   end-around-carry
                                   001   answer
```

Further examples of one's complements:

Given:	10	101	10110
One's complement	11	111	11111
	−10	−101	−10110
	01	010	01001

The real advantage of using the one's complement for subtracting binary numbers is that this complement is simply the inverse of the number being complemented. Examining the examples shows that the one's complement of 101 is 010, of 10 is 01, of 10110 is 01001. To obtain the one's complement, put a zero wherever a one appears and a one wherever a zero appears.

EXAMPLE:

```
  10001000   minuend
− 00010110   subtrahend (to be complemented)
```

Put zeros in every column, to match the minuend, then

```
   10001000
  +11101001   (one's complement)
 (1)01110001
      └────►1
   01110010   answer
```

D. BINARY MULTIPLICATION

Multiplication is accomplished in the binary system the same way it is accomplished in the decimal system, only more easily, since the only possible multipliers are a "one" or a "zero." No carries (within the multiplication) are produced until the final summation and then the regular rules for binary addition apply.

EXAMPLES:

```
  1101  =   13          10110
  ×110  =   ×6          ×1001
  0000                  10110
  1101                  00000
  1101                  00000
 ───────   ──          10110
 1001110   78          ──────
                      11000110
```

E. BINARY DIVISION

The process of binary division is the same as decimal division, only easier, since no possible quotient exists except a combination of "ones" and "zeros".

EXAMPLES:

$$
\begin{array}{r}
101 \\
101)\overline{11001} \\
101 \\
\hline
00101 \\
101 \\
\hline
000
\end{array}
\quad = \quad
\begin{array}{r}
5 \\
5)\overline{25}
\end{array}
$$

$$
\begin{array}{r}
1000.1001 \\
1100)\overline{1100111.0000} \\
1100 \\
\hline
0000111\,0 \\
110\,0 \\
\hline
001\,.0000 \\
1100 \\
\hline
0\,0100 \quad \text{remainder}
\end{array}
\quad
\begin{array}{l}
= \\
=
\end{array}
\quad
\begin{array}{r}
8.58 \\
12)\overline{103.000} \\
96 \\
\hline
70 \\
60 \\
\hline
100 \\
96 \\
\hline
40
\end{array}
$$

2-6 Conclusion

The previous arithmetic operations were illustrated using pencil-and-paper methods; machine (computer) methods were ignored. There are many ways a computer can be mechanized to produce the desired answers, and as a better understanding of logic and computer circuits is attained, it will be possible to examine arithmetic circuits and understand their operation. It would, of course, be impossible to check the correctness of these circuits unless pencil-and-paper techniques were mastered.

EXERCISES

1. Convert 5012_{10} to an equivalent binary value.

2. Convert 0.59375_{10} to an equivalent binary value. Limit the answer to five places.

3. Convert 11001101_2 to an equivalent decimal value.

4. Convert 0.11001_2 to an equivalent decimal value.

5. Add $100111_2 + 010011_2$

6. Add 1001_2
   001_2
   110_2
   10_2
   $+\underline{1010_2}$

7. Subtract 101010_2
   $\underline{-011001_2}$

8. Subtract $\quad 100010_2$
$$-\underline{001001_2}$$

9. Subtract $\quad 101110_2$
$$-\underline{011101_2}$$

10. Subtract by adding one's complement:
$$100010_2$$
$$-\underline{000110_2}$$

11. Subtract by adding one's complement:
$$101010_2$$
$$-\underline{011001_2}$$

12. Multiply $10110_2 \times 110_2$

13. Multiply $100010_2 \times 1001011_2$

14. Divide $1011_2 \div 11_2$

15. Divide (express to three places) $101001.01_2 \div 10101_2$

16. (*Optional*) Subtract $\quad 100111_2$
$$-\underline{101011_2}$$

17. (*Optional*) Convert 173_{10} to an equivalent base 5 number.

18. (*Optional*) Perform the following operation. Express the answer in decimal form.

$$213_8 + 1001010_2 = ?_{10}$$

3

LOGICAL ALGEBRA AND LOGIC EQUATIONS

3-1 Definition

Logical algebra is a method of symbolically expressing the relationship between logic variables. Ordinary algebra is the symbolic expression for relationship of number variables. Logical algebra differs from ordinary algebra in two respects:

(a) The symbols (usually letters) do not represent numerical values.

(b) Arithmetic operations are not performed.

Logical algebra was developed from the ideas expressed in *The Laws of Thought* written by George Boole in 1854. In recognition of his contribution, the term "Boolean algebra" is frequently used. Boolean algebra is an aid for analyzing many forms of logical thought and is ideal for describing the action of switching circuits. This application is important in computer design, since a switch may represent the characteristic "on" or "off" state of digital computer intelligence. The operation of a digital computer can be described by logical equations using Boolean symbology; hence, these equations are often referred to as the "computer logic."

3–2 Logical States

A. Two discrete states are considered to exist in logical algebra. Any pair of conditions different from each other could be chosen. The states are usually described as "true" or "false." A designer might choose any dissimilar value or state to represent "true," and any other to represent "false," and the ensuing design would be normally consistent in the use of these chosen values.

B. Every logical quantity must exist in one or the other of the two chosen states ("true" and "false"), and no other value is allowed.

C. Every logical quantity is single-valued. That is, no quantity may be simultaneously both "true" and "false."

D. Any quantity that is "true" is equal to any other quantity that is "true." Any "false" quantity is equal to any other "false" quantity.

E. Every quantity has an opposite. If the quantity is "true," then the inverse, or complement, is "false." If the quantity is "false," then the opposite is "true."

F. A logical quantity may be either constant or variable. If it is a constant, it is, and remains, either "true" or "false." If variable, it may switch between the "true" and "false" states from time to time, but only between these two extremes.

G. Logical quantities may be physically represented in many ways, such as:

(1) electrically, by two different voltages,

(2) mechanically, by the position of a toggle switch,

(3) optically, by the presence or absence of light,

3–3 Notations

As with ordinary algebra, the letters of the alphabet are usually used to represent logic variables. The letter A might represent the condition of a logic variable; and, in this case, the values A could assume would be only "true" or "false," since these are the only values a logic variable represents. In ordinary algebra, the letter A might represent any value from minus infinity to plus infinity. The symbol A' (A-prime), $\bar{A}$ (A-bar), or A^* (A-asterisk or A-star) will represent the inverse or complement of A. From the definitions of logic states, A and A^* cannot have the same value at the same time. Therefore, if A happens to be "false" at any given time, then A^* must be "true" at this time, and vice versa. The "prime" and "asterisk" signs are the most popular notations for the inverse condition since they are available on a typewriter.

If two or more logic variables are present at the same time, one might be represented by A, another by B, etc. If, at this time, B happens to be "true" and A happens to be "true," then $B = A$ since a "true" equals a "true." At this same time, the opposite of B is B^* and the opposite of A is A^* and $B^* = A^*$, because a "false" equals a "false." A moment later, the variable represented by A may change state and A then becomes "false" and A^* (the complement) becomes "true."

A^* (now equal to "true") $= B$ (still true), and

A (now "false") $= B^*$ (still false).

It is important to note that A, B, or B^*, etc are simply symbols to represent logic variables and that, at any given time, any symbol can be "true" and a moment later the same symbol be "false."

Generally, the symbol or letter "T" is reserved to denote the "true" state and "F" is reserved to denote the "false" state. Often 1 represents the "true" state and 0 represents the "false" state. 1 and 0 are popular because they are like binary numbers and are easy to write. Notice, however, that 1 is not necessarily equal to the number 1, and 0 is not necessarily equal to the number 0 unless proven to be so. The symbols, 1 and 0 only denote "true" and "false" *states* in *logical* variables.

For example, a designer might define as original conditions:

(a) "True" state—represented by T or 1 and equals – 5 V.
(b) "False" state—represented by F or 0 and equals 0 V.

Under these conditions, the binary number 10101 might be electronically represented on five different lines as shown in Fig. 3–1. Line C, for instance, might be given the logic notation C. When line C has a true voltage on it, $C = T = 1$, $C^* = F = 0$. When line C changes to zero volts, $C = F = 0$, $C^* = T = 1$.

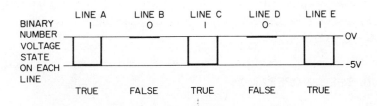

Fig. 3–1. Electrical representation of logical states.

3–4 Logic Operations

The operations that can be performed in ordinary algebra are multiplication, addition, subtraction, and division. In logical algebra there are three fundamental operations:

(1) The AND operation.
(2) The OR operation.
(3) The NOT operation.

In addition, there are two operations (or functions) that are accomplished by making certain combinations of the three fundamental operations. They are:

(1) The NOR operation.
(2) The NAND operation.

A. THE AND OPERATION

As in ordinary algebra, certain symbols are used to indicate the type of operation that is to be performed ($\times$ means multiply, $+$ means add, etc.). Symbology also exists for the logical operations. The AND operation is represented by a dot between the variables ($A \cdot B$). The AND function can be defined as follows:

(1) The function is true when all the ANDed logical quantities are true.
(2) The function is false when one or more of the ANDed quantities is false.

The AND function can be expressed as an equation: $f = A \cdot B^* \cdot C$ or AB^*C where f denotes the AND function. This equation would be read A and B not and C. Since this is an AND operation, the function will be true only when A is true, B^* is true, and C is true. If any or all of the variables become false, the function will be false.

Any combination of variables that are ANDed must follow the rules of the AND operation; hence, $A^*B^*C^*$ (A not and B not and C not) will yield a true output only when all the variables are true. This indicates that A must be false (A^* is true), B must be false (B^* is true), and C must be false (C^* is true).

B. THE OR OPERATION

The symbol that represents the OR function is a plus sign between the variables ($A + B$). The OR function is defined as:

(1) The function is true when one or more of the logical quantities is true.

(2) The function is false only when *all* of the variables are false.

The OR function can be expressed as an equation: $f = A^* + B^* + C$. The equation is read A not *or* B not *or* C. In this OR operation, the function will be true if A^* is true (A is false). The only conditions that yield a false output are that of A^* being false, B^* being false, and C being false, or that of all the variables that are ORed being false.

C. THE NOT OPERATION

The NOT operation is often referred to as negation or complementing. The negative of a quantity may be called the inverse, converse, or opposite. The NOT operation is indicated by a long bar over the logical quantity to be complemented. For example:

$$f = \overline{A^*} = A, \qquad \overline{A} = A^*$$

In the example above only a single variable was negated. If the term to be negated should contain an OR or AND operation in addition to the variables, this operation must also be complemented. For example:

$$f = \overline{A^* + B} = A \cdot B^* \qquad \text{and} \qquad f = \overline{A^* \cdot B} = A + B^*$$

Note that the complement of the AND operation is an OR and the complement of OR is an AND.

D. THE NOR OPERATION

As previously stated, the NOR operation is a combination of fundamental logical algebra operations. The NOR operation consists of the NOT and the OR operations. The term NOR is a contraction of the two words NOT OR. A NOR function can be defined as:

(1) The function is false when one or more of the logical variables is true.

(2) The function is true only when *none* of the variables is true.

Since the NOR function is NOT OR, it can be expressed by a logical equation consisting of the negation of an OR term.

$$f = \overline{A + B^* + C}$$

The equation output (f) will be true only when A, B^*, and C are false simultaneously (no variable is true). Further, f will be false when one or more of the variables is true. The function can be more readily understood by actually negating the function; thus:

$$f = A + B^* + C = A^* \cdot B \cdot C^*$$

Note that the negation of the OR terms becomes an AND function and, therefore, requires that A^*, B, and C^* must all be true $(A, B^*,$ and C are false) to yield a true output.

E. THE NAND OPERATION

The NAND operation is a combination of the NOT and AND operations. The term NAND is a contraction of NOT AND. The NAND operation can be defined as:

(1) The function is true when one or more of the variables is false.

(2) The function is false only when all of the variables are true.

The NAND function can be expressed as a logical equation as:

$$f = \overline{ABC^*}$$

Again, this is more readily understood by complementing the function.

$$f = A^* + B^* + C$$

The function will be true any time one of the variables $(A, B,$ or $C^*)$ is false $(A^*, B^*,$ or C is true).

Common circuits used to accomplish each of these operations will be investigated in a later chapter.

3–5 Truth Tables

Logical algebra, like any algebra or mathematics, is a tool used to solve a problem. Logical (Boolean) algebra is a tool used in solving logical problems. The truth table is useful as an aid for analyzing logical problems.

Although the table itself does not solve the problem, it offers a systematical approach by which all possibilities of the problem may be considered.

A. DESCRIPTION

The table consists of one "column" for each of the logic variables involved in a given problem. The "lines" of the table will be filled with all the possible true-false combinations the variables can assume with respect to each other. For instance, two variables can assume four different combinations at any of four different times, i.e., both true at the same time, both false at the same time, one true and one false, and vice versa. There are no other possible combinations. An additional column (or columns) will contain the function (*f*) under which the variables are to be considered. For example:

(1) The function column may contain the "output" when the variables are ANDed together.
(2) The *f* column may contain the "output" when the variables are ORed together.
(3) The *f* column may contain a particular "output" that must occur for each combination as stated by the given problem.

As an example, let us construct truth tables for some of the logical operations.

B. AND OPERATION

Use variables *A* and *B*.
Use switches A and B to represent the variables.
Use light L to represent the output.

By the definition of AND operation, the light L is on, or "true," when switch A is "true" AND switch B is "true." The switches may *arbitrarily* be considered "true" when closed, and "false" when open. Further, for simplicity in this example, let the symbol *A* represent the true condition and *A** the false condition; and the same for *B* and *B**. See Fig. 3–2.

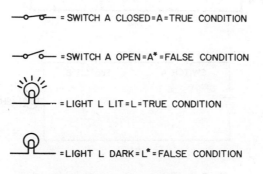

= SWITCH A CLOSED = A = TRUE CONDITION

= SWITCH A OPEN = A* = FALSE CONDITION

= LIGHT L LIT = L = TRUE CONDITION

= LIGHT L DARK = L* = FALSE CONDITION

Fig. 3–2. Symbolic switches.

Thus:

$$L \text{ (true) when } A \text{ (true) AND } B \text{ (true)}$$

or $L = A \text{ AND } B$

or $L = A \cdot B$

or $L = AB$

The truth table is shown in Fig. 3–3. Usually the truth table will appear simply as shown in Fig. 3–4A. The circuit representing this AND operation is a series circuit of switches A and B (Fig. 3–4B). The only time L is "true" (lit) is when both A *and* B are "true" (closed). These conditions occur in line 4 of the table.

	COLUMN VARIABLE	COLUMN VARIABLE	COLUMN OUTPUT
	SWITCH A	SWITCH B	LIGHT L ($A \cdot B$)
LINE 1	F	F	F
LINE 2	F	T	F
LINE 3	T	F	F
LINE 4	T	T	T

Fig. 3–3. Basic truth table.

	SWITCH A	SWITCH B	AB
LINE 1	F	F	F
LINE 2	F	T	F
LINE 3	T	F	F
LINE 4	T	T	T

L+AB

(A)

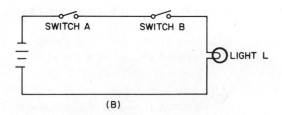

(B)

Fig. 3–4. AND-operation truth table and circuit.

C. OR OPERATION

Assume same conditions as before and:
> Use variables A and B (switches).
> Use light L.

Then L is "true" (lit) when A is "true" (closed) OR when B is "true" (closed), or

$$L = A + B$$

The truth table is shown in Fig. 3–5A. The circuit representing this OR operation is a *parallel* circuit using switches A and B (Fig. 3–5B). Light L is lit ("true") when either A or B or both are closed ("true"). These conditions occur in lines 2 through 4 of the table.

(A)

	SWITCH A	SWITCH B	OUTPUT L A+B	
LINE 1	F	F	F	
LINE 2	F	T	T	L=A+B
LINE 3	T	F	T	
LINE 4	T	T	T	

(B)

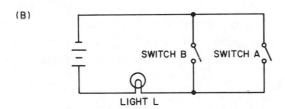

LIGHT L

Fig. 3–5. OR operation truth table and circuit.

D. THE NOR OPERATOR

The logical equation of the NOR function is

$$\overline{A+B} = L$$

Let A and B represent switches; let L = light on. This equation states that the light will be on only when A and B are false simultaneously. The equation also states that the light will be off when one, or more than one, of the input terms are true. The NOR function is seen as an

OR operation followed by a NOT (negate) operation. A truth table and the NOR circuit representation will usually appear simply as shown in Fig. 3–6.

SWITCH A	SWITCH B	L
F	F	T
F	T	F
T	F	F
T	T	F

$\overline{A+B}=L$

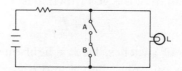

Fig. 3–6. NOR operation truth table and circuit.

E. THE NAND OPERATOR

The NAND logical equation is stated as

$$\overline{AB} = L$$

Let A and B represent switches; let L represent a light. The equation states that the light will be on if any one or all of the input terms are false. The light will be off when all of the logical terms are true. The NAND function is seen as an AND operation followed by a NOT (negate) operation. A truth table and simple switching circuit are shown in Fig. 3–7.

SWITCH A	SWITCH B	L
F	F	T
F	T	T
T	F	T
T	T	F

$\overline{AB}=L$

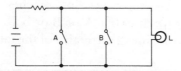

Fig. 3–7. NAND operation truth table and circuit.

F. LOGICAL PROBLEMS

Now let us use the truth table to help solve a logical problem. Suppose it is desired to control a light with two switches, A and B. The light is to be "true" (lit) when either of the switches (variables) is "true" but *not* when both of them are "true." The truth table (Fig. 3–8)

	INPUT COLUMNS		OUTPUT COLUMN	
	SWITCH A	SWITCH B	LIGHT L	
LINE 1	O	O	O	THE PROBLEM <u>STATES</u> WHAT THE OUTPUT
LINE 2	O	I	I	(FUNCTION) COLUMN
LINE 3	I	O	I	MUST BE
LINE 4	I	I	O	

Fig. 3–8. Sample problem truth table.

lists all possible combinations of the inputs A and B. The output column is filled according to the *conditions* of the problem. In this problem we have substituted 1 for "T" and 0 for "F." The only lines where the light is lit (1), which is the desired state, are lines 2 and 3. In line 4 each of the inputs is "true" (1); hence, the output is "false" (0) as the problem specifically says it should be.

We are attempting to write the logic equation, or proposition, for this problem, and from the equation mechanize a circuit of switches to fulfill the requirements of the problem.

Using the truth table as an aid, we obtain the following rules:

(1) Each entry line for which the value of the output is "true" represents one term in the equation to be written. This is so because the entries in that line have lit the light as we desired.

(2) Each equation term taken from a line with a "true" output consists of all the factors in that line being ANDed together. Every factor from the selected line is included in the ANDed term whether it be a "true" or "false" factor.

(3) All the AND terms taken from the selected lines are ORed together. This is so because line 2 OR line 3 causes the light to illuminate.

Applying these rules, we can then state the desired equation.

Light L is lit ("true") by lines 2 or 3

If we arbitrarily say that for this problem the symbols A^* and B^* are true, then:

Light L is lit when A AND B^* occur OR A^* AND B occur

or $L = A \cdot B^* + A^* \cdot B$

Finally, $L = AB^* + A^*B$

We may mechanize this equation in the manner used for AND and OR operations. We can use a single throw-double pole switch for both switch A and switch B that is arbitrarily "true" in one direction and "false" in the other (see Fig. 3–9). Since we are using both the "starred"

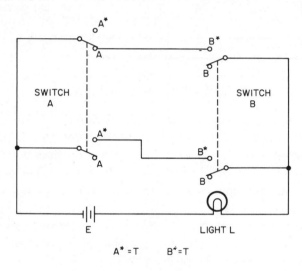

Fig. 3–9. Sample problem implementation.

and "unstarred" terms in our equation, we must allow for these conditions in the switches. The upper path is the mechanization (sometimes called implementation) of the term AB^*. Note that the "unstarred" or "false" (0) side of the switch A is connected to the "starred" or "true" (1) side of switch B in the manner dictated by the term. The lower path represents the second term A^*B and is connected by the same process as previously described. The switches are shown initially in the "F" position since logic is either "true" or "false" even at the start. They could have just as well been in the "T" position to start. Careful inspection of the circuit reveals that the light does not light either when both switches are "true" or when both switches are "false." Only when one or the other of the switches is true at a given time is the light energized.

Notice that the number of possible combinations of the variables in the table 2^n, where n is the number of variables; hence, two variables yield four combination lines, three variables (or three switches) yield eight combination lines, etc. A good way to assure the display of all possible combinations in the table is to determine the number of lines needed and perform a binary count from line 1 through line n. See, for example, Fig. 3–10, where the variables are $A, B,$ and $C,$ and the number of possible combinations $= 2^3 = 8$.

A	B	C	BINARY COUNT (DECIMAL EQUIVALENT)
O	O	O	O
O	O	I	I
O	I	O	2
O	I	I	3
I	O	O	4
I	O	I	5
I	I	O	6
I	I	I	7

Fig. 3–10. Total logical combinations. 1318138

As another example, suppose it is desired to control a light with three switches (Fig. 3–11). The light is to be on when one of the three switches is on but *not* when more than one is on. The manner in which the T or F sides of the switches are connected is dictated by the AND term that any given path of switches represents. That is, the top path (term $A*B*C$) goes from a star side to a star side to an unstarred side.

Notice that in each of the preceding examples the following items were present:

(1) Problem.
(2) Truth table.
(3) Logic equation.
(4) Mechanization.

These are the basic items with which computers and computer people are concerned. The problem may be anything the computer is asked to do; and it may be a mathematical, logistical, tactical, or general problem. In any case, the problem dictates the design and the use to which the computer is put. The table lays out the problem systematically; the

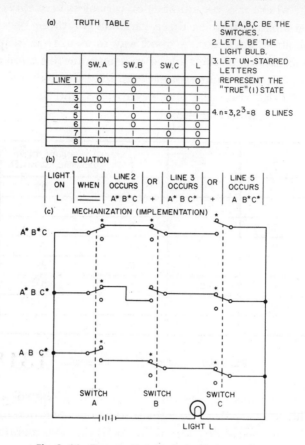

Fig. 3–11. From truth table to implementation.

logic equation or equations state the problem in logical algebra; and the mechanization (taken from the logic equation) *is* the computer.

Problems, truth tables, and logic equations do not, of course, physically exist in the computer, but they must be understood in order to build, operate, and repair the computer.

3–6 Logical Equation Simplification

To manipulate logic equations the unique properties of logic must be investigated. Logic variables obey the following identities and theorems.

A. IDENTITIES

The following equations represent a few of the more basic identities of logical algebra. They are identities by virtue of the rules of the AND and OR operations. That is, the equations are correct regardless of the values of the variables (A, B, and C).

These identities can be verified by substituting true and false values for the variables in each expression.

(1) $A + A^* = T$

(2) $AA^* = F$

(3) $AA = A$

(4) $A^*A^* = A^*$

(5) $A' + A' = A'$

(6) $A + AB = A$

(7) $A + A = A$

(8) $F + A = A$

(9) $TA = A$

(10) $T + A = T$

(11) $FA = F$

(12) $A + A^*B = A + B$

(13) $(A + B)(A + C) = A + BC$

To prove these identities, it is convenient to use the familiar "1" and "0" for "T" and "F." Remember, at the *start* of each exploration into quantities, it is necessary to define states. Where an identity is an absolute equality, it is insufficient to say that A in one identity equals A in another. Each identity must be defined as to the momentary state of its variables and each identity must then be proven independently. For the sake of simplicity, it is less confusing to decide that A shall be 1 or "true" and A^* shall be 0 or "false" and continue through the proofs in this manner; but satisfaction in the validity of these identities is gained by proving them with the variables alternately taking both states. Let us select a few and prove them.

(1)   No.(1) If A = 1 then A* must be the complement, or 0; thus, 1 OR 0 equals 1, which is defined as "true." Now, let $A = 0$ and then $A^* = 1$; then 0 OR 1 = 1, which is defined as "true." Hence, no matter which state the variables assume at any given time the output is always true.

(2)   Nos. (2), These are left for the reader to evaluate.
       (3), (4),
       (5), (7),
       (10)

(3)   No. (8) $F \equiv 0$.

$$\text{If } A = 0 \text{ then } (F+A) = (0 \text{ OR } 0) = 0 = A$$
$$\text{If } A = 1 \text{ then } (F+A) = (0 \text{ OR } 1) = 1 = A$$

Notice that even when "false" is represented by 1 (reversed), the identity still holds. That is, "false" $= 1$. Then if $A = 0$ (which is now "true"), then $F + A = 1 + 0$, which is "false," OR "true" $=$ "true," which is now $= 0$, which $= A$.

(4)   No.(11) $F \equiv 0$ and $T \equiv 1$.

$$\text{If } A = 0 \text{ then } (FA) = (0 \text{ AND } 0) = 0 = F$$
$$\text{If } A = 1 \text{ then } (FA) = (0 \text{ AND } 1) = 0 = F$$

(5)   No.(6) $F = 0$ and $T = 1$. If $A = 0$ and $B = 1$, $A + AB = 0$ OR 0 AND 1; 0 AND $1 = 0$. Hence, $A + AB$ now $= 0$ OR $0 = 0 = A$. If $A = 0, B = 0$, then $A + AB = 0 + 00 = 0 = 0 = A$. IF $A = 1$, $B = 1$, then $A + AB = 1 + 11 = 1 + 1 = 1 = A$.

All identities may be proven in this way. Numbers (12) and (13) are more easily proven by algebraic manipulations, which will be explained in the following discussion of theorems.

B. THEOREMS

The following theorems describe those properties of logical algebra that are similar to properties of ordinary algebra.

(1) The OR and AND operations are commutative. This is stated as follows:

$$A + B = B + A$$
$$AB = BA$$

(2) The OR and AND operations are associative.

$$(A+B) + C = A + (B+C) = A + B + C$$
$$(AB)C = A(BC) = ABC$$

(3) The OR and AND operations are distributive.

$$AB + AC = A(B+C)$$

As an example, prove identity No. (13).

$$\text{Does } (A+B)(A+C) = A + BC?$$

Apply theorem (3): $AA + AC + AB + BC = ?$

By identity (3), $AA = A$

By theorem (2), $(A + AC) + AB + BC = ?$

By identity (6), $(A + AC) = A$

By theorem (2), $(A + AB) + BC = ?$

By identity (6), $(A + AB) = A$

leaving $A + BC = A + BC$

Let us prove identity No. (12) in still another way. Refer to Fig. 3–12.

DOES $A + A^* B = A+B$?

A	B	A*	A*B	A + A* B	A + B
0	0	I	0	0	0
0	I	I	I	I	I
I	0	0	0	I	I
I	I	0	0	I	I
COL. I	COL. 2	COL.3	COL. 4	COL. 5	COL. 6

Fig. 3–12. Proof by truth table.

Columns 1 and 2 are all the possible combinations of variables A and B.
Column 3 is the complement of A (complement of column 1).
Column 4 is the AND of columns 2 and 3.
Column 5 is the OR of columns 1 and 4.
Column 6 is the OR of columns 1 and 2.

Column 5 $\equiv$ Column 6

The value of these identities and theorems is apparent when problems become more complex. More complex problems mean larger truth tables and more extensive logic equations. More extensive logic equations produce complex mechanization. Complex mechanization produces large and expensive computers. Obviously, it takes less switches to mechanize $A + B$ than it does to implement $A + A*B$. They are equal. Why use more switches? The computer designer investigates all logic equations and makes simplifications from known identities wherever possible.

An example will illustrate the use of the theorems for simplifying logical equations.

EXAMPLE:

Simplify the equation

$$f = AB + \overline{AB}CD + A\overline{BC} + \overline{A}C + ACD$$

Solution: Rearrange the terms and factor:

$$f = AB + A\overline{BC} + \overline{A}C + \overline{AB}CD + ACD$$

$$= A(B + \overline{BC}) + \overline{A}(C + BCD) + ACD$$

Apply identity (12) to $(B + \overline{BC})$ and identity (6) to $(C + BCD)$. Then:

$$f = A(B + C) + \overline{A}(C) + ACD$$

$$= AB + AC + \overline{A}C + ACD$$

Again rearrange the terms and factor:

$$f = C + AB + ACD$$

$$= (C + ACD) + AB$$

Apply identity (6) to $(C + ACD)$. Then:

$$f = C + AB$$

which is the simplest form of the original equation.

C. VEITCH DIAGRAMS

Veitch diagrams are an additional tool that may be used to simplify logical equations and may be constructed for any number of variables; however, they become more difficult to use as the number of variables increases. The Veitch diagrams for two through six variables are shown in Fig. 3–13. Since each variable has two possible states (true or false),

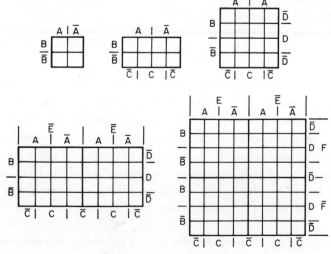

Fig. 3–13. Veitch diagram.

the number of squares required is 2^n, where n is the number of variables. Thus, for a three-variable Veitch diagram, there must be 2^3 or 8 squares.

To illustrate the use of Veitch diagrams for simplification, the logical equation $f = AB + ABCD + ABC + AC + ACD$ will be used (this is the same equation that was simplified by means of theorems).

Since there are four variables ($A, B, C,$ and D), the diagram must contain 2^4 or 16 squares. The procedure is as follows:

Step 1. Draw a 16-square diagram (Fig. 3–14A). (The number in each square is for discussion only.)

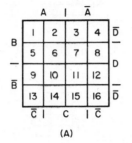 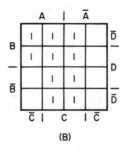

Fig. 3–14. Sample Veitch diagram.

Step 2. Plot the function on the diagram. This is done by placing a 1 in each square that is represented by the terms of the equation.

$$f = AB \ldots\ldots \text{squares } 1, 2, 5, \text{ and } 6$$
$$+ ABCD \ldots \text{square } 7$$
$$+ ABC \ldots \text{squares } 10 \text{ and } 14$$
$$+ AC \ldots\ldots \text{squares } 3, 7, 11, \text{ and } 15$$
$$+ ACD \ldots \text{squares } 6 \text{ and } 10$$

When the 1's are placed in the diagram, it appears as shown in Fig. 3–14B.

Step 3. Obtain the simplified logical equation from a Veitch diagram by following the four rules listed below. These same rules are illustrated in Fig. 3–15.

(a) If 1's are located in adjacent squares or at opposite ends of any row or column, one of the variables can be eliminated. The variable that may be dropped is the one that appears in both states ($\overline{A}$ and A).

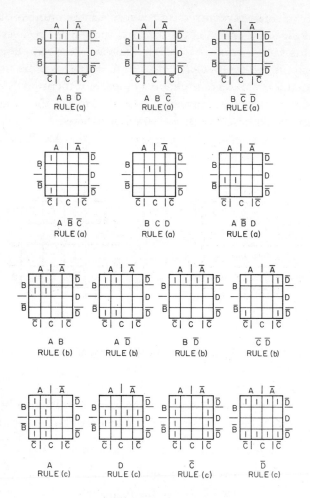

Fig. 3–15. Veitch combinations.

(b) Two variables may be dropped if there are all 1's in:

(1) any row or column of squares

(2) any block of four squares

(3) the four end squares of any adjacent rows or columns

(4) the four corner squares

The variables that may be dropped are those appearing in both states.

(c) Three of the variables may be dropped if there are all 1's in:

(1) any two adjacent rows or columns

(2) the top and bottom rows

(3) each square of both the right and left columns.

The three variables that may be dropped are those appearing in both states.

(d) To reduce the original equation to its simplest form, sufficient simplification must be made until all 1's have been considered in the final equation. Any of the 1's may be used more than once, and the largest combinations should be used.

Now the equation can be simplified: Squares 1, 2, 5, and 6 may be combined by using rule (b) and the variables C, C, D, and D eliminated, leaving the term $A \cdot B$.

Squares 2, 3, 6, 7, 10, 11, 14, and 15 can be combined using rule (c) and the variables A, A, B, B, D, and D eliminated, leaving only the term C.

All the 1's have been used; so the logical equation can be written in its simplest form:

$$f = A.B \pm C$$

which agrees with the simplification obtained by using the identities.

3–7 Conclusion

Points to remember:

(A) Logical states are two-way states, usually called "true" and "false." These two states can be accomplished in many ways, and either one of the states could be called "true" at the start of discussion, or design, and vice versa.

(B) Letters normally represent variables that are in one of the two states, either "true" or "false."

(C) There are five basic operations in logical algebra — AND, OR, NEGA-TION (often called NOT), NOR, and NAND.

(D) AA does not mean A times A and is not equal to A^2. AA means A AND A and should be verbally pronounced "A and A."

(E) $A + A$ does not mean A plus A and is not equal to $2A$. $A + A$ means A OR A and should be pronounced "A or A."

(F) There are 2^n possible "true-false" combinations of n variables.

(G) When we use the letter B (for example) as a symbol to represent a logic variable, no rule says that $B = T$ and $B* = F$. At any given time, B might be T and $B*$ be F; but a moment later B might be F and $B*$ be T. The *only* distinction is that $B*$ is the exact opposite of B, and $B*$ can never equal B at any given instant. However, for long discussions, or for proofs of logic equations, it is acceptable at the start to *assume* that, say, B be T and $B*$ be F, and maintain this fact throughout the discussion to avoid repetition. *But,* unless this assumption were known by a casual observer, he could not say whether B was "true" and $B*$ "false" or vice versa.

In succeeding sections we will investigate electronic circuits that may accomplish the logical operations (AND, OR, NEGATION, NAND, NOR) and circuits that may produce the logic states (TRUE and FALSE).

LOGICAL ALGEBRA EXERCISES

1. Why does the binary number system lend itself to use in a digital computer?

2. If $A* = $ False then A = _____ ?

3. If $A* = $ True then B* = _____ ?

4. What is the limit of the number of logic variables that may be ANDed together?

5. How many different combinations may be represented by four logic variables? Five variables? What is the maximum decimal number that may be represented by each?

6. List six physical phenomena which may represent logic algebra variables.

7. Negate the following (not operation)
  (a) $A \cdot B$
  (b) $(A + B)(C* + D)$
  (c) $A* + B \cdot C$
  (d) $(A \cdot B + C)D$

8. Complete the truth table for f.
  $f = A \cdot B + A*B*$

              A B f

9. Write an equation to describe f:

A	B	C	f
0	0	0	0
0	0	1	1
0	1	0	1
0	1	1	0
1	0	0	1
1	0	1	0
1	1	0	0

10. Write equations for the following switch networks.

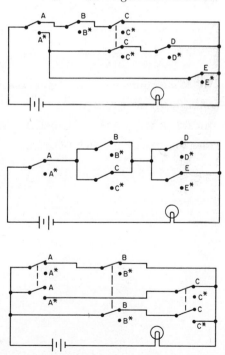

11. Simplify the following equations by using Logical Algebra.
(a) $f = (A+B)(A+B+C)(A+C)A*$
(b) $g = AB + AC + ABC + A*$
(c) $h = 1 + ABC(A+A*) + A*(AB* + AC*)$

12. Simplify the following networks by using Logical Algebra.

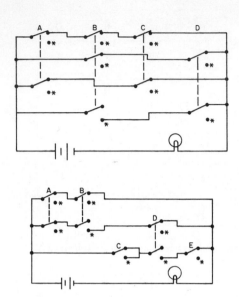

13. Simplify the following equations using Veitch Diagrams (show work).

$f = ABC* + A*BC + AB*C* + A*B*C$

$g = AC*D* + BCD(+ BAD* + A*BC + A*B*CD* + A*DC$

14. (Optional). Draw a five variable Veitch Diagram.

4

SEMICONDUCTORS

4-1 Introduction

This chapter offers a practical discussion of semiconductor devices (transistors, diodes, and microcircuits). The discussion is important to the reader who has had little or no opportunity to become familiar with these circuit elements that are used extensively in the mechanization of digital computers; vacuum tubes are practically nonexistent in present-day computers.

Since these elements are all constructed from solid, crystalline material that is neither a good conductor nor a good insulator and is neither in a vacuum, liquid, or gas, they are termed *solid-state* or *semiconductor* devices. The resistance of a good conductor is about 0.000002 ohms/cm³ and the resistance of a good insulator is about 9,000,000,000,000,000 ohms/cm³. The resistance of the crystalline material used for transistors is typically about 60 ohms/cm³ — therefore the term semiconductor.

The advantages of semiconductor devices over vacuum tubes become more apparent every day as new applications for these devices are found. They are smaller, less noisy, require no heater voltages, need less circuit power, are lightweight and rugged and have very good

47

reliability and long life. The chief disadvantages are that they must be protected from excessive heat and that they generally cannot carry the current demanded in some applications. As technology advances, these problems are being reduced, and semiconductor devices are being used in an ever-increasing variety of fields. In any case, their extensive use in computer circuitry requires further study.

4-2 Basic Solid-State Physics

Fundamentally, an atom is composed of a nucleus and a number of orbital electrons.

The nucleus is composed of neutrons (neutral particles) and protons (positive charges). The protons are in numerical balance with the electrons, which are arranged in shells about the nucleus. Thus the atom is electrically neutral unless an electron is forcibly added or removed, at which time the atom is said to be an *ion*.

Only a certain number of electrons can exist in the various shells about the nucleus. If the outermost shell contains the maximum allowable number of electrons, the atom is chemically and electrically inactive or inert. The first shell is complete with 2 electrons, the second with 8, the third with 18 or 8, the fourth with 32 or 18, etc. As indicated in Fig. 4-1, the helium atom has two electrons in its first (and only) shell and is

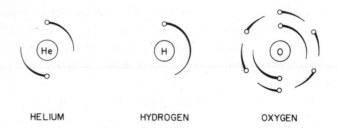

HELIUM   HYDROGEN   OXYGEN

Fig. 4-1. Atomic structure of sample elements.

an inert gas. The hydrogen atom has only one electron in its first (and only) shell, and would like to find another electron to complete this shell, it is, therefore, very active. Oxygen has six electrons in its outer shell, needs only two more to complete the shell, and hence is active in seeking these two electrons. Elements that have less than four electrons in a shell that is complete with eight, act as if there were no chance to gain six or seven electrons to complete the shell and, hence, tend to give away the few electrons they have to become a complete atom in terms of the next inner shell. These atoms are also active.

There are a group of elements, however, that have exactly half the required number of electrons in their outer shell and are no more inclined to give up their electrons than they are inclined to take electrons to become a complete atom. It is in this group that the semiconductor materials fall. Included are the common elements carbon (C), silicon (Si), titanium (Ti), and germanium (Ge), of which silicon and germanium have become the most used for construction of solid-state devices. These elements tend to bond together into symmetrical, crystalline structures.

A germanium crystal is formed when each Ge atom (with four electrons in its outer shell) shares its four electrons with adjacent Ge atoms. The electrons within a pure germanium crystal are bound in place and do not readily contribute to electrical conduction. Conduction requires current carriers that are mobile. However, if sufficient energy is applied to the crystal structure, an electron within a covalent bond will be dislodged. The energy required to break a covalent bond may be supplied by thermal or light energies. Thermal energy causes a crystal lattice to be in continuous random agitation, and room temperature is sufficient to free some electrons. This pure crystal, when agitated, displays a rather poor current-carrying capability that is no better in one direction than another. When an electron is dislodged and becomes a free current carrier, a hole that is capable of accommodating an electron is left in the crystal structure. If an electron moves from some other adjacent Ge atom to fill this hole, the hole will have effectively moved over to the atom that gave the electron. There are, therefore, both electrons and holes randomly drifting in opposite directions in a semiconductor crystal. Both are current carriers. If battery terminals are connected to an agitated semiconductor material, the holes will drift toward the negative electrode (and disappear when replaced by an entering electron from the battery) and the electrons will drift toward the positive lead.

The resistance of a pure semiconductor material depends on the number of electron-hole pairs generated for a given temperature. At room temperature, approximately one electron-hole pair is produced per 10^9 germanium atoms. The resistance of pure germanium at room temperature is about 60 ohms per cubic centimeter and the resistance of silicon is about 63,600 ohms per cubic centimeter. The difference is a function of the higher energy required to break a silicon bond; silicon is more stable than germanium.

The addition (doping) of impurity atoms to a crystalline semi-conductor greatly increases the material's conductivity. Light doping, about one impurity atom per 10^8 germanium atoms, will decrease the resistance of a cubic centimeter of germanium to 10 ohms or less. A doping element containing five electrons in its outer shell would fit into a germanium crystal structure but would have an extra electron left over (the crystal needs only four from each atom). This makes the crystal exhibit a negative character and increases its current-passing capability. Elements such as arsenic, phosphorus, and antimony have five-electron outer shells. When used to dope a semiconductor they are called "donors" since they give extra electrons to the crystal.

Semiconductors formed with a doping material containing less than four electrons in its outer shell have no extra electrons; in fact, they exhibit a positive character and have "holes" as the current carriers. The impurities creating this positive material are "acceptors" since they desire a free electron. Examples are indium, boron, and aluminum.

Crystal diodes and transistors are made by sandwiching together negative-doped (N-type) and positive-doped (P-type) semiconductor materials.

4–3 Junction Diodes

When a block of P-type crystal is joined to a block of N-type, the properties developed at the junction create a semiconductor device capable of rectification the same as a vacuum-tube diode.

The positive mobile carriers of the P-material are attracted by the negative mobile carriers of the N-material when the pieces are brought together. Near the junction, the mobile holes and electrons of the materials diffuse and combine with one another, effectively disappearing (encircled charges, Fig. 4–2). The diffusion of holes leaves an area of

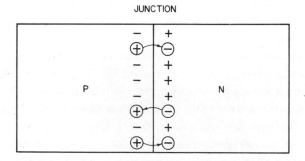

Fig. 4–2. P-N junction showing diffusion and barrier.

immobile negative ions in the P-material and the diffusion of electrons leaves an area of immobile positive ions in the N-material (uncircled charges, Fig. 4–2). The immobile charges repel the mobile carriers that would tend to continue diffusing across the junction. Finally, the P-N materials, joined together, become static with a current barrier at the junction. Nothing more than some random, drifting current will exist if the materials are agitated.

To cross the barrier at the junction requires a gain in energy, which can be obtained from a battery connected to the P- and N-materials. If the positive lead of the battery is attached to the P-material it will tend to push, or repel, the positive mobile holes of the P-material. The negative lead at the N-material has the same effect on the mobile electrons in the N-material. If the battery is of sufficient voltage (only very small voltage is needed), the mobile carriers will overcome the junction barrier and a current exists. This is called the forward-bias condition for a diode (Fig. 4–3B shows the normal schematic representation of the diode of Fig. 4–3A biased in the same way). If a diode is placed in a circuit

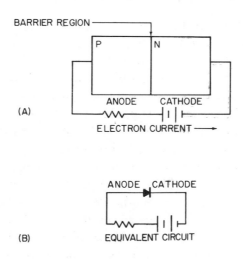

Fig. 4–3. Crystal diode, forward-biased.

with voltage applied in reverse (Fig. 4–4, P-material connected to negative battery lead, N-material connected to positive battery lead), the mobile carriers tend to draw away from the junction (circled charges). This force causes a widening of the barrier region resulting in a higher potential barrier, which in turn minimizes the number of carriers that are able to cross the potential barrier. This is called reverse-biasing or back-biasing a diode, and causes the diode to offer maximum resistance to external current.

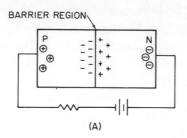

(A)

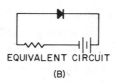

EQUIVALENT CIRCUIT

(B)

Fig. 4–4. Back-biased diode.

If the quantity of voltage used to back-bias a crystal diode is made larger and larger, a point will be reached where the large resistance presented to the reverse voltage is overcome and the large reverse current suddenly occurs. The negative lead of the battery has essentially become so strong it has reached across and crushed the mobile negative carriers out of the N-material while the positive lead has done the same to the mobile carriers in the P-material. When the point of breakdown has been reached and reverse current occurs, the diode exhibits what is essentially a constant voltage source; that is, reverse resistance goes down as reverse current goes up after breakdown has been exceeded. This is the same phenomena that occurs in a gas tube regulator. Sufficient back voltage to produce reverse current will ruin many types of crystal diodes not constructed to withstand the resulting heat; however, diodes of a certain class are specially constructed to withstand and take advantage of the effects of reverse current. Called Zener diodes, these are used in circuits as voltage-regulating devices. The behavior and breakdown point are reproducible, with conditions returning to normal when the bias (battery) is removed. Some of the more common schematic representations for Zener diodes are shown in Fig. 4–5.

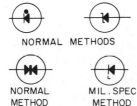

NORMAL METHODS

NORMAL METHOD   MIL.SPEC METHOD

Fig. 4–5. Common Zener diode schematic symbols.

4-4 The Transistor

The transistor is a logical extension of the junction diode and is analogous to the triode vacuum tube. Essentially it consists of two junction diodes with half of each diode forming a common element. Figure 4-6 illustrates the two basic types of transistors. N- and P-materials are sandwiched together into either NPN or PNP configurations, and ohmic connections made to each material to form a transistor. This sandwiching is not a literal joining together of three materials, but rather a chemical process that maintains a single crystal pattern throughout. The emitter (analogous to the cathode of a vacuum tube) and the base (analogous to the grid) can be regarded as one of the two junction diodes. The second junction diode is formed by the base and collector (the collector is analogous to the vacuum-tube plate). In the absence of external voltage, the two junctions within the transistor exhibit energy barriers not unlike those exhibited by the previously discussed junction diode.

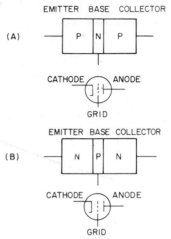

Fig. 4-6. Basic PNP and NPN transistors.

To be conducting, the junction between the emitter and base must be forward-biased, while the junction between collector and base is reverse-biased. For a PNP transistor, as shown in Fig. 4-7, this means the emitter is positive with respect to the base and the collector is negative with respect to the base. These polarities are reversed for an NPN transistor. Only the PNP transistor will be discussed in detail since the mechanics of both types are identical; only the voltage polarities are opposite.

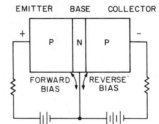

Fig. 4-7. PNP transistor biased for conduction.

Assume the emitter of a transistor is disconnected and the collector-to-base junction is reverse-biased. This would result in no current or an insignificant collector current consisting only of a slight reverse diode current (see Fig. 4-8). Now assume there is a method of placing many holes in the base region. These holes (carrying the properties of a

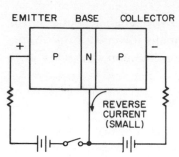

Fig. 4-8. Reverse collector current.

positive charge) would be attracted to the negative terminal of the collector's power source and produce a collector current, dependent upon the number of holes placed in the base. The function of the emitter of a PNP transistor is to place more or less mobile carriers in the base region (in this case, holes).

When a transistor is connected for conduction as illustrated in Fig. 4–7, the forward-biased emitter-base junction forces many holes into the base region and, in a junction diode, these holes that pass from the P-material into the N-material would soon disappear through the battery lead connected to the base. However, by making the base of the transistor very narrow and doping it lightly, all the holes emitted into the base do not have a chance to pass to the base lead before the majority of them have been attracted to the potential attached to the collector.

The complete picture of the current in the PNP transistor under these conditions is shown in Fig. 4–9. Some base current does exist

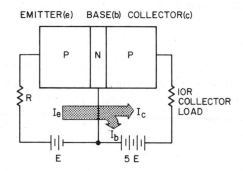

Fig. 4-9. Current paths in a conducting PNP transistor.

(that is, the base potential captures some mobile carriers), but most of the current moves through to the collector lead. The most current in the device exists in the emitter, which is supplying the large quantities of mobile carriers.

Although the picture representation of a transistor shows it as a symmetrical device, this is not true in reality. The transistor is usually "grown" or produced from a basic semiconductor material, and the sizes and chemical dopings of the three elements (base, emitter, and collector) are different. The actual sizes and makeup depend on the uses or type of transistor desired; in general, the emitter is doped more heavily than the collector (since it must "emit" a large quantity of mobile carriers) and the base is doped to a value creating the desired barrier potentials between the two junctions (emitter-to-base and collector-to-base). The collector is usually larger in area than the emitter. As may be realized, connections could be made causing the collector to assume the emitter's role and vice versa. In many transistors this will do no material harm, except that, of course, the transistor will not perform as it was designed to. With some transistor types, a reversed connection will affect or destroy the transistor.

Besides the difference between the physical characteristics of an actual transistor and its picture representation, it is important to notice the electrical characteristics that provide the transistor with its element of basic usefulness: the ability to amplify. As shown in Fig. 4–9, less current is actually entering the collector than left the emitter, but, the collector current is able to pass through a much higher resistance (collector load) than the emitter current since the collector potential is higher than the emitter potential. Therefore, the power available in the collector circuit $(P = I^2R)$ is much greater than that in the emitter circuit. The schematic symbols of transistors are shown in Fig. 4–10.

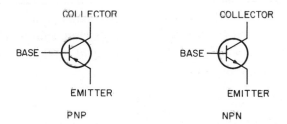

COLLECTOR

BASE

EMITTER

PNP

COLLECTOR

BASE

EMITTER

NPN

Fig. 4–10. Transistor schematic symbols.

As with vacuum tubes, there are three basic circuit configurations for transistors. Table 4–1 gives the analogies of these circuits with vacuum-tube circuits, and also indicates common names and usages.

Although the emitter and collector currents are practically independent of collector voltage, they are not entirely so. The thickness of the collector junction increases with an increased collector voltage. This, in turn, decreases the number of carriers lost due to recombination, because the distance in which recombination can take place is reduced. Higher collector voltage therefore causes a slight collector-current increase. The collector voltage also effects the emitter current. Increased collector voltage causes a slight increase in emitter current. All the carriers emitted into the base region neither recombine nor enter the collector material. A few of these carriers diffuse from the edge of the emitter junction back into the emitter material. An increased collector voltage increases the hole concentration in the base, which, in turn, increases the rate of holes diffused toward the collector, this results in a decrease in the number of holes returning to the emitter.

TABLE 4-1 Circuit Configurations

TRANSISTOR CIRCUIT	*VACUUM-TUBE CIRCUIT*
Common Base Base grounded, signal usually applied to emitter. Produces low-gain and low-noise signal. Collector output not inverted.	*Grounded Grid* Grid grounded, signal to cathode. No inversion on plate out. Low-gain, low-noise configuration.
Common Emitter Emitter grounded, signal applied to base. Normal amplifier connection. High gain. Inverted output on collector.	*Grounded Cathode* Normal amplifier configuration. High gain. Signal applied to grid. Inverted output on plate.
Common Collector Collector grounded, signal applied to base. Output across emitter. No gain. Impedance match to following stage, emitter follower.	*Grounded Plate* Plate grounded, signal applied to grid. Output taken from cathode. No gain. Impedance match to following stage, cathode follower.

However, virtually all the collector current in the PNP transistor is a function of the holes produced by the emitter and diffused through the base. It follows, therefore, that any change in the emitter-base bias will have a strong effect on collector current. In other words, the difference of potential, or bias, between emitter and base has the major control over the amount of current through the transistor.

The collector current will be approximately the same regardless of the size of the resistance placed in the collector circuit. By varying the emitter-base bias, as with an AC signal, the collector current will vary in proportion. By choosing a large collector resistance it is possible to attain large voltage and power amplification. Figure 4–11 is an example of typical values used in a transistor amplifier and shows the amplification realized.

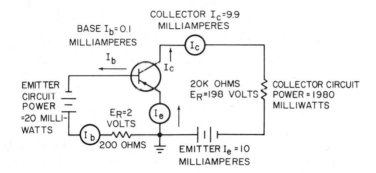

Fig. 4–11. Typical PNP transistor amplifier.

When the forward bias of the emitter-base junction is increased, a point will be reached where the emitter is producing as many holes as possible without excessive heating. When this point is reached, the transistor is said to be *saturated,* and any increase in emitter-base bias (within safe degrees) will not increase the collector current

If, as in Fig. 4–11, the emitter is grounded and ground is applied to the base, the bias between emitter and base is zero. There is no for-ward-bias across the junction between emitter and base and, since forward-bias is the criteria for conduction in a transistor, this transistor is said to be at the cut-off point. If the bias between emitter and base becomes reversed, the transistor is further cut off (for the transistor in Fig. 4–11 this would be a positive voltage on the base with zero on the emitter). The transistor must have forward bias between emitter and base to conduct. Would the transistor in Fig. 4–12A be conducting? In Fig. 4–12B?

In Fig. 4–12A the bias (difference between emitter and base DC potentials) is 3 V; more important, the emitter is 3 V more negative than the base or, in other words, the base could be considered to be zero and the emitter − 3 V, creating the same effect. This creates a bias between the emitter and base junction as shown in Fig. 4–13A (reverse-biased);

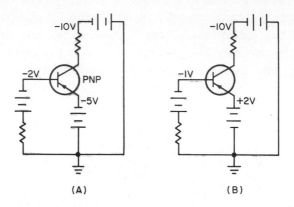

Fig. 4–12. Typical bias problems, PNP transistors.

hence, the transistor is definitely cut off. Fig. 4–12B also has a bias of 3 V, but the potentials created are as shown in Fig. 4–13B, (forward-biased); hence, the transistor in Fig. 4–12B is definitely conducting.

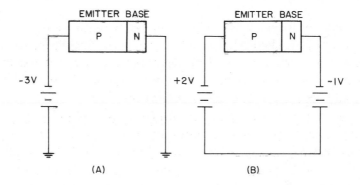

Fig. 4–13. Emmiter-to-base bias examples − PNP transistor.

It is very important to be able to recognize the voltage conditions that create cut-off or saturation in a transistor, because these two conditions represent the most common usage of a transistor in digital devices.

By operating transistors at saturation or cut-off, a switching circuit is produced. This is a frequently employed circuit in modern computers.

It is easily recognized that since this produces one of two states or conditions, it readily lends itself to binary numbering systems and logical algebra.

In a computer that uses a negative voltage to represent a "true" level, it is most likely that primarily PNP transistors would be used. The PNP transistors will be connected to potentials so that the true level (minus voltage) when applied to the base will cause them to saturate and zero volts will cause them to cut off. If a computer were to have a positive voltage to represent a "true," it is expected that NPN transistors would be used extensively. In this case, the "true" level (now a positive voltage) would again cause the transistors to saturate and the zero volts cause them to cut off. How these transistors are mechanized into various circuits will be the next item of study.

4–5 Basic Transistor Circuits

As a working example, examine the circuits and waveshapes in Fig. 4–14 showing transistors (PNP and NPN) used as grounded-emitter amplifiers. These circuits are analogous to the grounded-cathode vacuum-tube amplifier.

The input signal is applied to the base (grid).
The output signal is taken across the collector (plate) load.

For these circuits it is assumed that 0 V to the bases, or grid, keeps the elements cut off and the ±5 V signal is sufficient to cause saturation. For the example's sake, it was desired to hold the outputs between ground (saturation condition) and some clamp value. Investigating the PNP circuit we notice that ground (0 V) to the base is zero bias between emitter and base junction (treated as reverse-bias); hence, the transistor is cut off. With the transistor cut off, the clamping diode feels −10 V on its cathode and −5 V on its plate, which causes conduction and places nearly the clamp value of −5 V at point A. When the transistor receives −5 V to its base it has a strong forward-bias between emitter and base junction, causing immediate saturation. With the transistor saturated, nearly ground potential is transmitted up to point A, which makes the output nearly ground and also reverse-biases the clamping diode, cutting it off.

Notice that the NPN and vacuum-tube circuit have the same polarity relations. Their analysis is the same as for the PNP circuit with

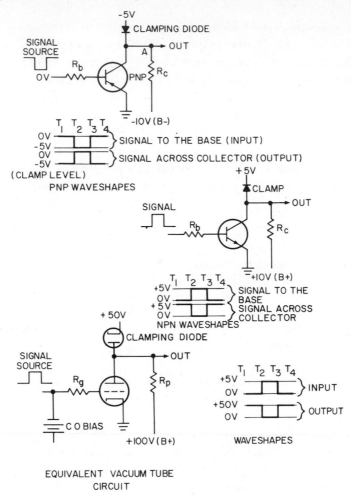

Fig. 4–14. Grounded emitter transistor amplifiers.

reversed voltage polarities. Figure 4–15 shows the common outline configurations for transistors. Notice that the actual size of most transistors is about that of a pea.

4–6 Integrated Circuits

The recent development of integrated (micro) circuits is creating dramatic changes in the electronic and computer-equipment industry. In much the same manner that the invention of the transistor, over 15 years ago, reduced the size and increased the reliability of electronic circuits, the invention of integrated circuits (often called "solid circuits") again

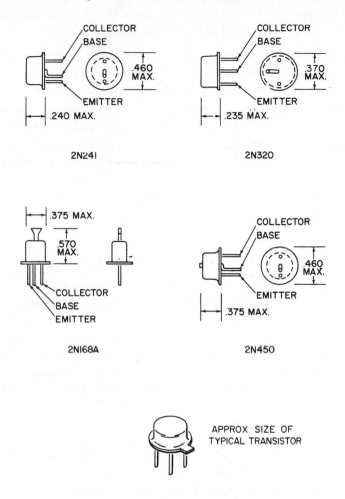

Fig. 4–15. Common transistor configurations.

greatly reduces the size, the power requirements, and in some cases the cost of electronic circuits, as well as increasing their life and reliability. These new circuits will reduce the size of equipment that is now as large as a file-cabinet drawer to matchbox proportions.

An integrated circuit serves all, or the major part, of a given circuit's functions, and is constructed from a single small piece of material. The complete packaged size of an integrated multivibrator circuit need be no larger than the single transistor shown (approximately actual size) in Fig. 4–15. Typical electronic equipment, using transistors, would require approximately $2 \times 2 \times \frac{1}{2}$ inches for the same type circuit. Currently, the two basic techniques for producing integrated circuits are:

A. A *thin-film process* by which passive components (capacitors resistors, and so on) are deposited as material layers onto an inert substrate (such as glass). This process uses multiple evaporation, spattering, or vapor decomposition to deposit the passive circuit components. The quantity, or mass, of material deposited would, for example, determine the size of a resistor. Active elements (transistors) must be attached separately to the film circuits. Although this type of integrated circuit must obviously be somewhat larger than a single transistor, the range of values for the passive elements is wide, external wiring is avoided, compactness and high reliability are achieved, and the over-all size is much less than that of a normal circuit.

B. A *semiconductor-device* (or *single-block) technology*, by which both active and passive devices are formed (essentially grown) within a tiny block of undoped silicon semiconductor material. Transistors are created by doping small portions of the material, making N-type regions, and sandwiching them into transistors. Resistors are made from selected volumes of either N- or P-material (semiconductor material exhibits known amounts of resistance), and capacitors are formed around selected areas of P-N junctions. Diodes are available from the numerous junctions of P-N material existing in the block after selective doping.

4–7 Mechanization Process

The semiconductor technology utilizes multiple masked diffusion, surface-layer passivation, and metal film alloying to create and connect all active and passive elements in the one tiny block (chip) of material. Although the over-all circuit produced is very small and rugged, the ranges of component values are somewhat more restricted than in standard circuits or in thin-film circuits, and reasonably large values of inductance are, as yet, difficult to obtain; however, most standard digital circuits use little or no inductance.

The decided advantage of the solid-block integrated circuit is that thousands of a given circuit can be mass-produced from a few basic P-N junction wafers yielding a finished chip (individual) no bigger than a large pin head.

The following example indicates the method for creating a two-transistor, two-resistor, one-capacitor circuit by the single-block technique

A. Figure 4–16A shows the basic wafer composed of a layer of N-type silicon grown on a P-type silicon substrate. The wafer is protected

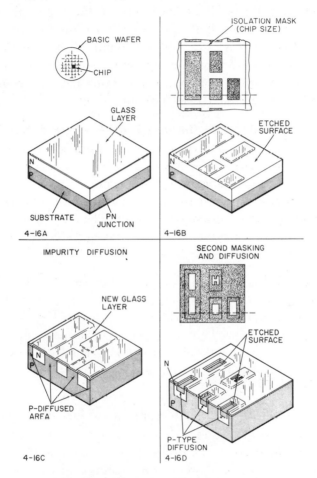

Fig. 4–16. Integrated circuit development.

with a silicon dioxide (glass) layer. During the building process, the entire wafer is divided into a number of chips, each chip becoming a complete circuit. The number and size of chips per wafer are determined by the circuit complexity desired. The indicated wafer and subdivision of chips in Fig. 4–16A are approximately the actual size of typical solid-block integrated circuits.

B. Figure 4–16B shows a mask that isolates the areas selected for building the two transistors, two resistors, and the capacitor. The mask is laid over the wafer, and the protective glass is etched away everywhere except at the selected areas. This prepares the end-type material for isolated diffusions.

C. Diffusing P-type impurities (Fig. 4–16C) into the exposed. N-type substrate creates all P-type material except for those regions under the selected areas. The isolated islands of N-type silicon thus formed make possible the creation of multiple components on the same chip with no unwanted common connections between components. A new glass layer is deposited over the entire wafer.

D. Figure 4–16D shows the second mask-off for etching and subsequent diffusion of more P-type material. Windows are etched at locations suitable for forming transistor bases, whole resistors, anode portions of diodes, and junction-type capacitors. This P-type diffusion is of much shorter duration than the first diffusion. As the diffused material enters the wafer it also diffuses laterally, forming each junction at the surface under a protective portion of glass layer. A new glass layer is again coated over the surface.

E. The new glass coating is again etched out at selected window areas and a short-duration diffusion of N+ (heavily concentrated negative impurities) material forms transistor emitter areas, cathode regions for diodes and capacitors, and layers for circuit contacts and crossovers (Fig. 4–17A). The N+ material is used since transistor collectors are doped at a lesser concentration than emitters. A new glass layer is coated over the entire wafer.

F. As shown in Fig. 4–17B, the patterns are etched all the way down to the material upon which electrical connections will be made. A metal deposit will be made over the entire wafer, providing the conducting material for connections between components and external circuitry. This even coating of material will be etched away except where connections are desired (Fig. 4–17C). Notice the "large" pads provided for external connections (about the size of a period). Some metal-layer areas may be left to form glass-dielectric capacitors in conjunction with the underlying substrate.

G. At this point, the process is essentially complete. The wafer is scribed into individual circuits (chips) that are bonded to a ten-lead header (Fig. 4–17D). The external solder points of the chip are wired to leads on the header and a cap is welded on, providing a hermetic seal

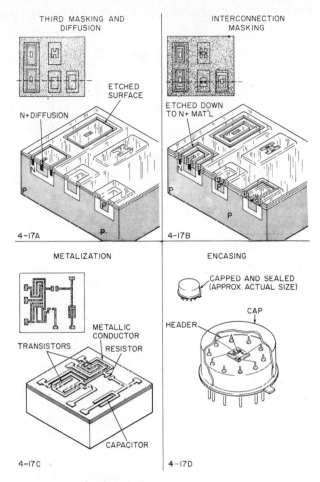

Fig. 4–17. Integrated circuit development.

for the circuit. This not only creates a sealed, rugged circuit producing reasonably large leads for manual soldering, but also establishes a universal component much like a transistor.

There are various forms of integrated circuits currently on the electronic market. One manufacturer pots the chip into a very small, flat rectangle with solder leads protruding from each side. Since the basic transistor already has proved to have a life of many years (some have never failed in ten years of continuous use), it is safe to assume that the integrated circuit will extend this reliability factor to the entire circuit. Mass-production runs on common circuits will also reduce the cost of electronic equipment, and the savings in size and power requirements are obvious.

EXERCISES

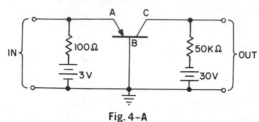

Fig. 4–A

1. The transistor shown in Fig. 4–A is NPN type or PNP type

2. Element A of the transistor in Fig. 4–A is the
   (a) Base
   (b) Collector
   (c) Emitter
   (d) Cathode

3. With respect to the base, the emitter of the transistor in Fig. 4–A is
   (a) forward biased
   (b) reverse biased
   (c) open
   (d) unbiased

4. Under static conditions, the transistor in Fig. 4–A is
   (a) cutoff
   (b) conducting

5. A minus 3-volt signal applied to the input of the circuit in Fig. 4–A will cause the transistor to be
   (a) conducting
   (b) cutoff

6. If the circuit shown in Fig. 4–A has small signals applied to its input the outputs will be
   (a) Inverted
   (b) Noninverted

7. The circuit configuration in Fig. 4–A is a
   (a) grounded emitter amplifier
   (b) grounded base amplifier
   (c) grounded collector amplifier

8. A P-type material has been doped to contain

    (a) Donor atoms

    (b) Acceptor atoms

9. Label the three leads of the transistor shown in Fig. 4–B.

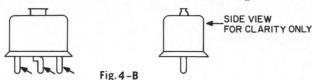

Fig. 4–B

10. Integrated circuits promise to make computers

    (a) smaller and lighter

    (b) more reliable

    (c) cheaper

    (d) all of the above

11. In the following circuit show the bias batteries and polarities so that the transistor will conduct.

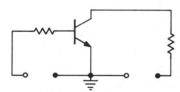

12. Draw the output waveshape. Label the voltages. (A difference of potential of three volts is sufficient to saturate the transistor.)

13. Draw the output waveshape for the circuit as shown. Label output voltage.

5

CLAMPS AND GATES

5-1 Introduction

The functions (AND, OR, and so on) of digital computers are implemented by various electronic circuits. The most basic of these are the diode clamps and diode gates.

5-2 Clamps

There are two basic types of clamps (also called limiters):

(A) The series clamp.

(B) The shunt clamp.

Both types serve the same purpose, which is the limiting of a portion of the input signal. The circuit usually contains a diode and a resistor arranged in a configuration that depends on which portion of the input signal the clamp is to limit. The diode used is the active clamping (limiting) element, and the resistor is the load, or signal-developing, element. If the active element (diode) is in series with the signal line, the clamp is a series clamp; if the active element is in parallel with the line, the clamp is a shunt clamp. There may be two types of both series and shunt clamps as shown in Fig. 5–1. The operation of all clamps is similar; therefore, the following description includes only the upper series clamp and the lower shunt clamp. The same technique may be applied to the other clamps.

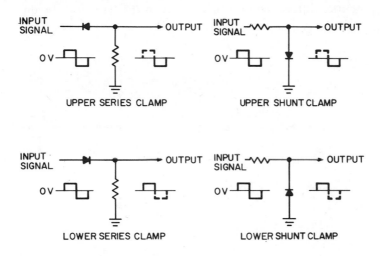

Fig. 5–1. Clamp configurations.

5–3 Upper Series Clamp

When the input signal to the clamp (as shown in Fig. 5–1) is positive, the diode is back-biased. In this state, the diode appears as an open switch and does not allow the signal to pass. When the input signal goes negative, the diode is forward-biased. The diode then appears as a closed switch and the input is dropped (developed) across the resistor.

5–4 Lower Shunt Clamp

When the input voltage is positive, it back-biases the diode and the diode appears as an open switch, allowing the input to pass unaltered. When the input voltage is negative, it forward-biases the diode, causing the diode to appear as a closed switch which shunts (shorts) the input to ground.

5–5 Clamp Application

Figure 5–2 shows a possible application of diode clamps. The shunt clamp is used here to limit positive- and negative-going voltage excursions. This example is based on the following arbitrary assumptions:

A. Transistors Q1 and Q2 shall be cut off by 0 V on the base and saturated by −4 V on the base.

B. A potential difference of ±10 V between the base and the emitter of Q2 will damage the transistor.

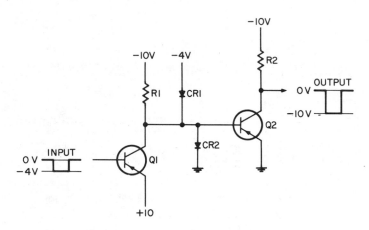

Fig. 5–2. Sample use of the clamp.

When 0 V is applied to Q1 (transistor cut-off) without the clamps CR1 and CR2 in the circuit, −10 V (with respect to ground) would appear at the base of Q2 and damage the transistor. CR1, however, is forward-biased by the −10 V and appears as a closed switch shorting out all but −4 V, which passes on to the base of Q2, turning Q2 on. CR2 is back-biased and appears as an open switch, exerting no influence on the circuit. When Q1 is turned on by a −4-V input, +10 V would tend to appear at the base of Q2, but CR2 is forward-biased by the +10 V and shunts it to ground, passing 0 V to the base of Q2 and preventing transistor damage. At this time, CR1 is back-biased by the +10 V and appears as an open switch, exerting no influence on the circuit. Thus, by the use of diode limiters, the desired circuit operation is achieved without transistor damage.

5–6 Gates

A gate, as used in computers, is a circuit configuration that accomplishes a logic operation (AND or OR). That is, an AND gate will pass, or yield, a true output when all inputs are true. An OR gate will yield a true output when any input is true.

There are many electrical devices that will accomplish these operations, but since gates constructed of solid-state devices have become almost universal, they are the only type that will be discussed. All computer gating concerns itself with only two possible inputs or voltage levels (logical "true" and "false"). At any given time one of these two inputs can be present on any input line to the gate.

5-7 AND Gates

The most common logic symbols for an AND gate are shown in Fig. 5-3. In the illustration, $A, B, C, \ldots$ are inputs, and the output is

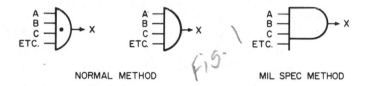

NORMAL METHOD　　　　　　　　MIL SPEC METHOD

Fig. 5-3. AND gate logic symbol representations.

X. The equation would be $X = ABC \ldots$ Theoretically there is no limit to the number of inputs to a gate circuit, but normally the number of inputs allowable is restricted by loading characteristics. A maximum of from six to eight inputs is not uncommon. The military specification gate configuration uses an extension of the input face for more than three inputs to leave room on the drawing.

Remember that we need handle only two distinct states. Assume two distinct voltage levels: 0 V and −5 V. First assume 0 V to be the "true" level. It follows, therefore, that the inverse of 0 V must be "false." False must equal −5 V. A three-input diode AND gate, following these assumptions, is illustrated in Fig. 5-4A. Inputs $A, B,$ and C must exist at either −5 V or 0 V. True has been defined as 0 V. Assume point $A = 0$ V; $B = 0$ V; $C = -5$ V. Under these conditions, diode C will be the most forward-biased and appear as a closed switch. This will place point X at −5 V and back-bias diodes A and B. The output, X, will equal −5 V and, therefore, be false. Assume all inputs equal 0 V (true). In this case, all diodes will be forward-biased an equal amount and will appear as closed switches. This will produce a potential of O V at point X—a true output. Note that this is the only combination of inputs that will yield a true output. Other inputs using combinations of true and false can be similarly analyzed. Note, too, that all requirements of the AND definition are satisfied. The only time a true output is produced is when *all* inputs are true. Any other input combination produces a false output.

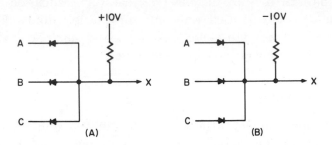

Fig. 5–4. AND gate schematic representations.

Using the same voltage levels as before, 0 V and −5 V, Fig. 5–4B illustrates the construction of an AND gate when the negative voltage is considered true. Under these conditions the inverse of −5 V (true) will be 0 V (false). Since the true level has now been defined as −5 V, the AND definition states that point X shall equal −5 V only when A, B, and C all equal −5 V, and point X shall equal 0V under any other input conditions. Points A, B, and C must equal 0 V or −5 V. True is defined as −5 V. Assume point $A = -5$ V; $B = -5$ V; $C = 0$ V. Under these input conditions, diode C will receive the most forward-bias and appear as a closed switch. This will place point X at 0 V and back-bias diodes A and B. The output, X, will equal 0 V and be false.

Assume all inputs equal 0 V (false). In this case, all diodes will be forward-biased an equal amount, and will appear as closed switches. This will produce a potential of 0 V at point X — a false output.

The only combination of inputs that will produce a true output of −5 V is that all inputs equal −5 V and, therefore, all inputs are true.

Although AND gates employing solid-state diodes can be mechanized in several ways, each way must meet the requirements established by definition: an AND gate is a circuit that will produce a true output only when all the inputs are true.

Therefore, in design or analysis of AND circuits, several questions must be asked. What are the two voltage levels involved in these circuits? Which voltage level is considered to represent "true"? How may the diodes be connected to fulfill the requirements of an AND circuit?

Either Fig. 5–4A or Fig. 5–4B illustrates the correct electrical

schematic of an AND gate, depending upon which voltage level represents "true." Regardless of which levels are used, Fig. 5–4A is always
correct when the more positive level is true, and Fig. 5–4B is correct
when the more negative level is true. For example, the voltage levels
used could be: +100 V and +80 V; −50 V and −30 V; +10 V and −10 V;
etc.

Most recent computers use the more negative level as true. It is
suggested, therfore, that study be concentrated on the type of AND gate
exemplified by Fig. 5–4B. In either case, the logic symbol and logic
equation remain the same.

5–8 OR Gates

An OR gate is defined as a circuit that will produce a true output if
any one, or if all inputs are true, and a false output only when all inputs
are false. The most common logic symbols for an OR gate are shown in
Fig. 5–5. In the illustration, $A, B, C, \ldots$ are inputs, and the output is X.

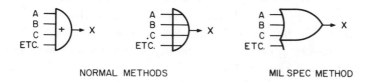

NORMAL METHODS   MIL SPEC METHOD

Fig. 5–5. OR gate logic symbol representations.

The equation would be $X = A + B + C + \ldots$. The two voltage levels used
in the following analysis of OR gates will be the same as those previously
used with AND gates: 0 V and −5 V.

Assume the condition where 0 V is considered true and −5 V is
false. A diode OR gate constructed to fulfill the definition requirements
is shown in Fig. 5–6. Assume the following inputs: $A = 0$ V; $B = -5$ V;

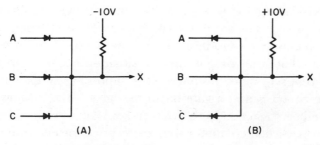

Fig. 5–6. OR gate schematic representations.

$C = -5$ V. Under these conditions, diode A will receive the most forward-bias and appear as a closed switch. This will cause 0 V to appear at point X and back-bias diodes B and C. B and C will, therefore, appear as open switches and exert no influence on the output of the circuit. The output, X, will appear as 0 V and be true. Other possible inputs combining true and false can be similarly analyzed.

Assume that inputs A, B, and C are all equal to -5 V (false). All diodes will then be forward-biased an equal amount and will appear as closed switches. A potential of -5 V will appear at point X, which is a false output. This is the only combination of inputs that can possibly produce a false output from this gate. Thus, the definition requirements of an OR gate are met.

Conversely, it can be assumed that the negative potential -5 V represents true and 0 V represents false. Examination of Fig. 5–6B shows an OR circuit fulfilling the definition requirements when the more negative level is considered true.

Assume the following inputs: $A = -5$ V, $B = 0$ V, and $C = 0$V. Under these conditions, diode A will receive the most forward bias and appear as a closed switch. This will pass -5 V and produce a true output.

Assume that inputs A, B, and C are all equal to -5 V (true). All diodes will then be forward-biased an equal amount and will appear as closed switches. A potential of -5 V will appear at point X—a true output.

Assume that inputs A, B, and C are all equal to 0 V(false). All diodes will be forward-biased an equal amount and will appear as closed switches. A potential of 0 V will appear at point X—a false output. This is the only combination of inputs that can produce a false-output from this gate.

Therefore, the requirements of the OR gate definition have been met: the gate produces a true output if any, or if all inputs are true, and a false output only when all inputs are false. Since most modern computers use a negative voltage for true and ground for false, emphasis should be placed on the circuit configurations used when the more negative potential is considered true (Fig. 5–6B). It is important to notice that what is an OR gate in one situation becomes an AND gate for a different set of circumstances. It is impossible to tell whether any given gate circuit is an OR gate or an AND gate without knowing what states have been assigned to the voltage levels of a given computer. Of course, any particular computer will usually be consistent, using particular AND-OR gates throughout.

Although all preceding illustrations have indicated three inputs to the gates, the inputs are not necessarily limited to three. The maximum number of inputs that can be used depends on parallel resistances, current capacities, individual diode characteristics, the load of the circuit that will accept the gate's output, and other factors beyond the scope of this discussion. Less than two inputs would not constitute a true gate.

5–9 NOT Circuit

The NOT circuit is included in this discussion of gates, because, like the gates, the circuit implements one of the basic logic functions (negating). A brief explanation of the process of negating (inverting) is necessary at this point to simplify the discussion of NOR and NAND circuits that follows. A NOT circuit is required to provide a false output whenever the input is true, and a true output whenever the input is false.

Ordinarily, a single-stage grounded-emitter amplifier is adequate to provide logic inversion. When a negative-voltage state is true, a PNP transistor will be used, since minus voltage causes the transistor to conduct, creating a ground (0 V) output that is the opposite of the minus input voltage. If a computer uses a positive voltage for the true state, an NPN transistor would be used for the inverter circuit. A simple PNP transistor NOT circuit for a negative-voltage true system is shown in Fig. 5–7.

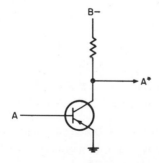

Fig. 5–7. Sample NOT circuit.

When the input to the circuit is true ($A = -V$), the negative voltage on the base will turn on the transistor and cause electrons to flow from the negative source to ground, causing a large voltage drop, compared to the transistor across the resistor. The output voltage with respect to ground is negligible (or nearly ground) and is assumed to be false (0 V). If the input A is false (0 V), the transistor is cut-off, conduction will not occur, and the output will be a negative voltage, i.e., a true state. A more typical inverter circuit will be covered in detail in the next chapter.

5-10 NOR Circuits

The NOR circuit performs the logical NOR function discussed in Chapter 3. The schematic, Fig. 5-8, shows that the NOR circuit is an OR circuit followed by a NOT (negating) circuit. To completely analyze the NOR circuit, the following assumptions must be considered:

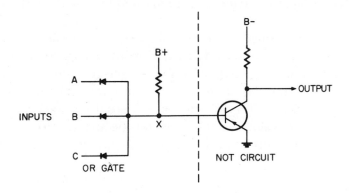

Fig. 5-8. NOR circuit schematic representation.

Assumption I: All inputs are false (0 V).
Assumption II: Inputs A and B are false (0 V) and C is true ($-$V).
Assumption III: All inputs are true ($-$ V).

Point X is the output of the OR circuit and will be false (0 V) when all inputs are false, or true when one or more of the inputs is true (negative voltage). The inverter output will be the opposite condition that appears at point X. If the inputs happen to be $A*$, B, $C*$, these logic variables will be $A*+B+C*$ at point X and will next be inverted $(\overline{A*+B+C*})$ yielding $AB*C$ at the output. Figure 5-9 shows some common logic symbols used to represent the NOR gate.

5–11 NAND Circuit

A typical NAND circuit is shown in Fig. 5–10 for a system using negative voltage for true and 0 V for false. Examination of the figure shows

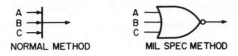

NORMAL METHOD   MIL SPEC METHOD

Fig. 5–9. NOR circuit logic symbol
representation.

that it contains an AND gate with R3 as the pull-down resistor; a bias
network of R1, CR1, and R2; and an inverter (NOT) circuit.

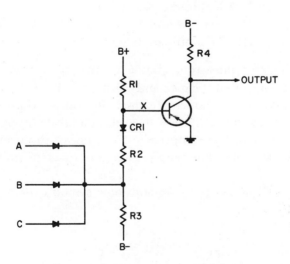

Fig. 5–10. Typical NAND circuit schematic
representation.

The bias network of R1, CR1, and R2 is needed in this circuit when
the assumed (given) logic levels are negative volts for true and 0 V for
false. If we pick approximately −5 V = T, 0 V = F, close inspection of
the AND gate used for these logic levels reveals that although the two
possible outputs of true and false are theoretically said to be −5 V and

0 V, actually the two values might be about −5.5 V and −0.5 V owing to the small forward resistance that does in reality exist in the diodes used in the gate. The bias network creates a very small positive value at the transistor base when 0 V (actually about −0.5 V) is the logic output of the AND gate. This ensures cut-off of the transistor. Looking back at Fig. 5–8, we notice that the OR gate for "negative level true" logic works into a pull-up (to B+) resistor, and owing to the slight forward resistance in the diodes, the outputs at point X actually vary between something less than −5 V and some slight positive value (which is theoretically said to be ground). In this case, no biasing network is needed between the OR gate and the inverting transistor. If the given logic levels were reversed, a biasing network would be needed in the NOR gate but not in the NAND gate.

To analyze the NAND circuit, the conditions associated with each of the following assumptions must be considered.

Assumption I: All inputs are true (−V).
Assumption II: Inputs A and B are true (−V) and C is false (0 V).
Assumption III: All inputs are false (0 V).

With all gate inputs true, a minus voltage will appear at point X as a result of the output of the gate and biasing circuit. This condition will cause the transistor to conduct, creating a 0 V output (false). Keeping A and B true but making C false will result in a false output of the gate, and will cause point X to approach 0 V, causing the transistor to be reverse-biased (cut-off). The output then goes to a true (minus-voltage) condition.

Figure 5–11 shows the common logic symbols used to represent the NAND gate.

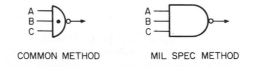

COMMON METHOD   MIL SPEC METHOD

Fig. 5–11. NAND circuit logic symbol
representations.

5–12 Uses of the NOR and NAND Circuits

The object of considering the NOR or NAND circuit when designing a computer is that either type of circuit can replace both the AND and OR gate functions. Consider the equation:

$$X = A*BC + B*D + AC*D*$$

that, implemented by AND and OR functions, would be as shown in Fig. 5–12A. This implementation requires four gates: three AND gates and one OR gate. Implementation of the same equation could be done using five NOR gates as shown in Fig. 5–12B. The NOR and NAND gates provide amplification out of the transistor which the passive diode

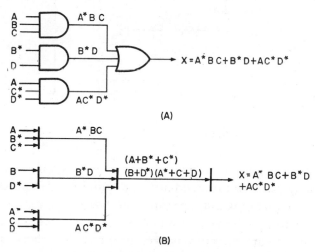

(A)

(B)

FIVE NOR GATES REPLACING "AND" AND "OR" FUNCTIONS

Fig. 5–12. Uses of the NOR gate to perform AND and OR functions.

constructed AND and OR gates do not. Although this particular equation required one more gate when implemented NOR, in most cases where an entire computer is constructed of all NOR gates, they can inexpensively be mass-produced for the given computer to accomplish all of its necessary gating and also provide signal amplification. The result usually represents a savings for a given machine, since this amplification would have to be provided by other circuits in an AND-OR computer.

5–13 Special Gates

(A) INHIBITOR GATE

It may be desirable in the design of a computer to produce a singular pulse output that is controlled by another voltage level. In this circuit, a pulse input is to be passed directly to the output unless the control pulse is present. This is mechanized by an inhibitor circuit (inhibitor gate). The inhibitory pulse is sometimes referred to as a suppressor, or prohibitory pulse.

Figure 5-13 is an example of an inhibitor gate. Assuming −5 V

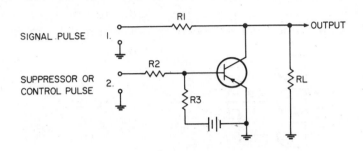

Fig. 5-13. Inhibitor gate schematic.

is true and 0 V is false, note that whenever −5 V is applied to input 1, approximately −5 V will be read across R_L (output). If, however, −5 V is applied to input 2, it will overcome the battery potential and cause the transistor to operate at saturation. At saturation, the transistor has low resistance characteristics; hence, it effectively shorts the pulse applied at input 1 to ground and thus inhibits the appearance of a pulse at the output.

(B) EXCLUSIVE OR GATE

At times it is very desirable to have a special type of two-input OR gate where the output is false when both inputs are false, the output is true when either input is true, but the output is false when both inputs are true. This is an exclusive OR gate. The logic symbols most commonly used for an exclusive OR gate are shown in Fig. 5-14.

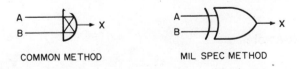

COMMON METHOD   MIL SPEC METHOD

Fig. 5-14. Exclusive OR gate logic symbols.

The truth table for the exclusive OR condition is shown in Fig. 5–15. A circle around the + sign denotes the exclusive condition. The equation for lines 2 and 3 is:

$$\text{ouput} = A'B + AB'$$

where A arbitrarily $= 1$, $A' = 0$; B arbitrarily $= 1$, $B' = 0$. The output column represents the exclusive OR condition, hence:

$$\text{output} = A + B \quad (A \text{ "exclusive or" } B)$$
$$A + B = A'B + AB'$$

	A	B	A⊕B
LINE 1	0	0	0
LINE 2	0	1	1
LINE 3	1	0	1
LINE 4	1	1	0

A⊕B IS TRUE ONLY WHEN ONE INPUT IS TRUE BUT NOT WHEN BOTH ARE TRUE

Fig. 5–15. Exclusive OR gate logic truth table.

To mechanize this equation will take two AND gates (terms 1 and 2) and an OR gate (the AND terms are ORed together). The inputs to the AND gates are A and B' to one, and A' and B to the other. Symbolically, the circuit would appear as shown in Fig. 5–16.

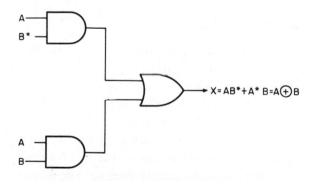

$$X = AB^* + A^*B = A \oplus B$$

Fig. 5–16. Exclusive OR gate implementation.

As an explanation, consider the case where:

$$A = 1 = T, \quad \text{then } A' = 0 = F, \quad \text{and at the same time}$$
$$B = 1 = T, \quad \text{then } B' = 0 = F$$

The inputs to both AND gates are then T · F, which equals F. The output X is then F.

Consider the case where:

$$A = 1 = T, \quad \text{then } A' = 0 = F, \quad \text{and at the same time}$$
$$B = 0 = F, \quad \text{then } B' = 1 = T$$

The input to the top AND gate in this case is T · T = T output; hence, the final output is $X = T$.

Although the exclusive OR gate is in reality made-up of AND gates and OR gates, it will have its own logic symbol if it is used enough in a particular computer. As will be seen in later chapters, this exclusive OR condition is often used in arithmetic circuits; hence, the special symbol. The exclusive OR is only a sample of many special gates that may have individual logic-gate symbols although created from standard AND and OR gates. The source of logic voltages (A, A', B, B') shown in Fig. 5–9 will be covered in later discussions.

By definition, an exclusive OR gate is limited to two inputs. More inputs can be mechanized by feeding the output of one exclusive OR gate as an input to a second exclusive OR gate (Fig. –17).

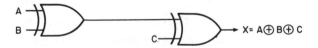

Fig. 5–17. Exclusive OR gate uses.

5–14 Purpose of Gates.

The design of complex computers is based on the AND and OR principle. AND and OR gates are used to decode electrical impulses on many lines and reduce these to an impulse on one line only. Gates tell a computer, by their outputs, when to perform an operation, where to find some particular information, when to proceed, when to stop, where to store information for future use, and, in fact, direct every conceivable operation a computer can perform. To keep track of these complexities, it is common practice to assign a type of nomenclature to various signals. This lends itself, very naturally, to the utilization of logical algebra. For example, examine the Boolean equation $X = ABC + DE + FG + H$. By making some assumptions, a practical application of this equation may be conceived. Assume a complex computer that contains, as part of its output equipment, an electric typewriter. Assume the signal X tells this typewriter to type the letter "Y." Translated, what does this equation say? The equation speaks to the circuits controlling the typewriter and says, "There are five conditions under which you shall cause the letter Y to be typed." They are as follows:

1. If signals A, B, and C are present at the same time;

2. Or if signals D and E are present at the same time;

3. Or if signals F and G are present at the same time;

4. Or whenever signal H is present;

5. Or if all previously mentioned signals are present at the same time.

It is obviously more convenient to run only one wire from the computer to the typewriter to type the letter Y. The signal on this wire is called, for identification, X. This circuit could be mechanized as shown in Fig. 5–18.

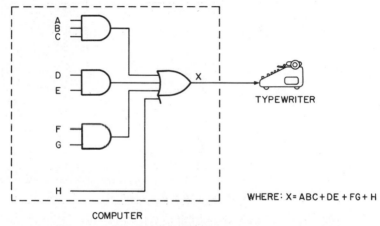

WHERE: X = ABC + DE + FG + H

COMPUTER

Fig. 5–18. Implementation using logic symbols.

Large, complex, high-speed electronic computers, covering hundreds of square feet of floor space, all contain, in common with all other computers, certain basic circuits. These few basic circuits, plus any special circuits to perform the specific job of the computer, are then interconnected by the AND and OR principle to form the modern— complex — computer.

EXERCISES

1. Using shunt clamps draw a circuit to limit a signal to between −3 V and +5 V.

2. Draw a series clamp that allows only signals greater than +5 V to pass.

3. Complete the following truth table for an AND gate.

A	B	C	f
0	0	0	
0	0	1	
0	1	0	
0	1	1	
1	0	0	
1	0	1	
1	1	0	
1	1	1	

4 Draw the electrical circuit for an AND gate (−3 V false, 0 V = true)

5. Draw the electrical circuit for an OR gate (−3 V = false, 0 V = true)

6. Draw the logical schematic, using AND and ORgate symbols, to mechanize the equation X = ABC + D + E*F + G*. (Assume all signals and complements are available.)

7. Assuming logical levels of *True* = −3 volts and *False* = 0 volts, draw an electrical schematic to mechanize equation X of Ex. 6.

8. Write a logic equation for the output *N* of the NOR network in Fig. 5–A.

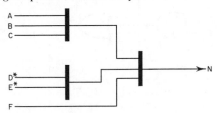

9. Draw the logical schematic, using only NOR gates, to mechanize the equation for X in Ex. 6.

10. Write the logic equation for the output, *M*, of the NAND network in Fig. 5–B.

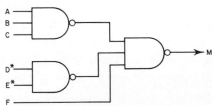

11. Complete the following truth table for an "exclusive OR" gate.

A	B	f
0	0	
0	1	
1	1	

6

FLIP-FLOPS, INVERTERS, AND BOOSTERS

6-1 Introduction

In addition to the AND or OR gates, three other elementary logic circuits are used in most computers: the flip-flop, the inverter, and the booster. Within the computer there are, of course, power supplies, and many special-duty circuits, yet the logic work of the computer is borne by these three circuits and the gates discussed in Chapter 5.

6-2 The Flip-Flop

The flip-flop, or bistable multivibrator, has two outputs, each at a different level. The two outputs will remain unchanged unless the proper voltage is applied at the flip-flop inputs. The bistable multivibrator, with its two-level, stable output states, is an ideal circuit with which to implement the true-false conditions of computer logic. A simplified multivibrator circuit is shown in Fig. 6-1.

The two back-to-back halves (A and A') of the circuit are identical and would conduct an equal amount were it not that one tube is bound to have inherently better conducting characteristics, and greater conduction by one tube reinforces the cut-off state of the other tube.

Such factors dictate that the circuit will quickly come to the static condition of having one side conduct while the other side is cut-off.

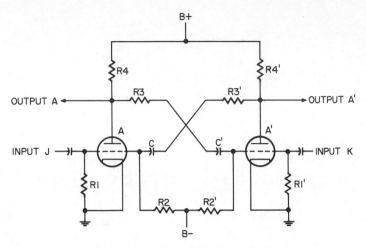

Fig. 6–1. Simple multivibrator circuit.

If tube A is conducting and tube A′ is cut-off, output A is nearly at ground potential while output A′ is nearly at the B+ potential. Capacitor C is initially charged to the positive value at output A′ and capacitor C′ is charged nearly to the ground potential at A. Under these conditions, a positive trigger at input K would cause A′ to conduct, creating a momentary ground at the A′ output load, thus allowing C to discharge through R2. The discharge of C causes a negative drop to occur across R2, cutting off A. At the same time, C′ begins to charge to the rising positive value of output A. The rising charge on capacitor C′ tends to drive A′ to saturation, although the positive trigger fed into input K may now be gone. The flip-flop has now reversed its state (A is positive and A′ is approximately at ground) and will stay in this new condition until another proper input is again applied. The "proper" input would be either a positive trigger at input J or a negative trigger at input K.

A simplified flip-flop using transistors is shown in Fig. 6–2. Like the tube-design flip-flop of Fig. 6–1, the transistor stages conform to a balanced design. The collector output of Q is fed to the base of Q′ through C′ and R_1′, and the output of Q′ is fed to Q through C and R_1. As with the preceding circuit, in the static state, one transistor conducts while the other is cut-off. The conducting transistor will have approximately ground potential at its output, and the transistor at cut-off will have some negative value at its output. These contrasting values can be used for the equally contrasting "true-false" values of computer

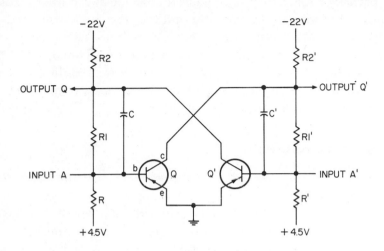

Fig. 6–2. Simple transistorized flip-flop.

logic. In fact, these output voltages will usually be clamped (Chapter 5) to a given voltage value to conform to the selected logic level of the computer. Since the transistors used in this example are PNP devices, a negative trigger at the base (of a nonconducting transistor) is required to cause conduction.

The logic symbol for a flip-flop (shown schematically in Figs. 6–1 and 6–2) is given in Fig. 6–3. The symbol is usually a box or rectangle with the two inputs generally entering from the left side, and the two outputs leaving the right side. However, for simplification, in many logic diagrams the input/output leads may

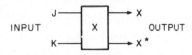

Fig. 6–3. Flip-flop logic symbols.

enter or leave from any side. The X designates the flip-flop's number and/or location, which could be any number or any location. Hence, wherever X appears, the flip-flop designation will be written in. X might be FF01 (flip-flop number one) and the outputs would then be FF01 and FF01'. The FF may be dropped, since it is understood that a box is a flip-flop. X may also refer to "A12," meaning that this is flip-flop number 12 located in the amplifier section. The outputs would then be labeled A12 and A12'.

The output lines, X and X′, are *always* in opposite states. The X and X′′ notations *do not* indicate the particular state (either true or false) at a particular time; they only indicate that the two output leads are opposite. As indicated by Figs. 6–1 and 6–2, the two output leads can vary from one to the other state from time to time. The J and K letters designate the two possible input leads, where J is defined as the "set" input and K is defined as the "reset" input. Some flip-flops designate the set input with an S and the reset input with an R. In many systems, a Q is synonymous with the X used in Fig. 6–3.

6–3 Flip-Flop Logic

A flip-flop normally will be designed such that the logic voltage levels of a given system are of sufficient amplitude to act as the trigger

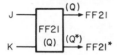

Fig. 6–4. Flip-flop symbol example.

inputs. The logic of a flip-flop describes the output state for different combinations of input states. The flip-flop operating conditions for the example shown in Fig. 6–4 are as follows. Given -5 V $=$ T, 0 V $=$ F:

1. If J is "true" and K is "false," Q (FF21) will go "true" (if it is not already "true," in which case nothing happens).

2. If J is "false" and K is "true," Q′ (FF21′) will go "true."

3. If both J and K are " false," the flip-flop will remain as it is.

4. If both J and K are "true" at the same time, the action may be indeterminate; hence, J and K are usually never allowed to be "true" simultaneously.

We may investigate these conditions on a truth table (Fig. 6–5). Notice that it must be known what state the output is in at the time a "T" or "F" pulse is applied to the input. It is customary to present a column with the Q output state at time n, and another column with the output state after the input pulse has acted on the flip-flop (designated time $n + 1$). All of the conditions that the Q output may be in at time n are accounted for, and all the combinations of inputs for these existing outputs are shown; hence, the flip-flop conditions at $n + 1$ are also accounted for. The Q′ outputs are, of course, in the opposite states, and hence a Q'_{n+1} column is not needed in the truth table. Notice that the outputs are only changed by *"true"* input signals to one input or another. That is, if output Q is "true," a "true" at side J has no effect;

also a "false" at J has no effect. Only a "true" action at K can cause the FF to flip when a true already exists at output Q.

Qn	J	K	Qn + I
I	O	O	I
I	O	I	O
I	I	O	I
I	I	I	NOT ALLOWED
O	O	O	O
O	O	I	O
O	I	O	I
O	I	I	NOT ALLOWED

Fig. 6–5. Flip-flop logic truth table.

By definition, the Q (unprimed) output of the FF is called the "set side" or "set output." The Q' (primed) output is called the "reset output." Since it is customary to draw the FF logic diagram with the Q output above the Q' output, the two output leads are often informally referred to as the "high" and "low" outputs. Since there is no "rule" that the logic diagram must be drawn this way (it only has to be labeled correctly), it must be understood that the term "high" output refers to the Q or "set" side.

Therefore, a true or 1 on the J input (S input) "sets" the flip-flop (Q output = T = 1); a true, or 1, into the K input (R input) "resets" the flip-flop (Q' = T = 1). It follows that a flip-flop that is "in the set state" (or a "high" FF) has a true on its Q output and a false on its Q' output and vice versa.

6–4 Flip-Flop Types

Actually, the J and K labeling of the flip-flop inputs designates a type of flip-flop. The JK flip-flop was especially designed for early digital computers. The JK flip-flop will accept the "true-true" input configuration and will flip. However, determination of the set or reset condition of the output states would then require prior knowledge of the output states at the time before the "true-true" was applied. Since this proved to be cumbersome from a logic designer's standpoint, it became standard practice not to allow the 1-1 input condition to occur. As this became a generally accepted and workable rule, it was next decided not to bother designing a flip-flop that would flip when the 1-1 input occurred (which requires extra components), but rather to have a flip-flop that is absolutely indeterminate when this condition exists. The RS type flip-flop is indeterminate when the 1-1 input occurs because it lacks the necessary components to flip; hence, the 1-1 input is never allowed with this type of flip-flop. Actually, most recent digital computers use true RS type flip-flops but maintain the JK input designation letters because they have already been used in most of the system's early documentation.

Among other types of flip-flops used in computer design is the $K\overline{K}$ (K-K bar) flip-flop. There is only one input lead (K) and this lead is internally split, one side passing directly in (K), the other being inverted before becoming an input ($\overline{K}$). The K input (internal) is considered as the J input (Fig. 6–6). Whereas it takes an active influence (a "true" signal)

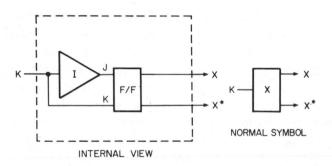

INTERNAL VIEW   NORMAL SYMBOL

Fig. 6–6. $K\overline{K}$ flip-flop.

to change the state of a JK or RS flip-flop, it takes only a change of state of the input to change the output state of a $K\overline{K}$ flip-flop. That is, the first "true" voltage in a series of true voltages sets the $K\overline{K}$ flip-flop, and not until a zero (false) occurs, does the flip-flop reset.

Another type of flip-flop often used in digital systems is called the override flip-flop. This flip-flop will normally operate with a steady true signal on its K input so that it is usually reset (it is always attempting to reset). When a true signal arrives at the J input (a 1-1 condition), this true signal will override the 1 on the K side and "set" the flip-flop. This flip-flop will immediately reset when a 1 no longer appears on its J input.

There are many other types of flip-flops commonly used in digital computers. However, all digital-type flip-flops incorporate essentially the same circuitry with minor differences.

A flip-flop may often assume a special name in several places throughout the computer to designate its specific use, although usually it is still a basic type with only a few minor changes to satisfy the surrounding circuit requirements.

6–5 A Typical Digital Flip-Flop

Figure 6–8 shows a high-current flip-flop that is used in a tactical data system computer. Assume transistor Q3 to be conducting. Since Q3 is conducting (base-emitter junction forward-biased), the collector current will be at saturation and the collector voltage will be V_{sat} (which is essentially ground potential). Coupling to the base of Q4 is accomplished through divider chain R11, R12 (which is returned to a pull-up voltage, +4.5V). In this manner, the base voltage of Q4 becomes more positive and Q4 is thereby cut-off (reverse-biased). With Q4 cut-off, its collector voltage is held, by action of the load resistor R9 and clamping diode CR5, at the clamp voltage, −4.5 V. Return coupling from the collector of Q4 to the base of Q3 is accomplished through divider chain R7, R8, causing Q3 to be conducting, as originally assumed. Also, it is noted that when Q3 is conducting, the collector voltage (in this case V_{sat}) is coupled through a network comprised of R13, L2, C5, and R14 (which is returned to a +4.5 V) and voltage reference diode CR9, thereby cutting off Q5. The current from the collector load (R15) of cut-off Q5 is diverted through R16 to the base of transistor Q6. The action of current through R15 and R16 puts a negative potential on the base of Q6, causing Q6 to conduct. With Q6 conducting, the collector voltage becomes V_{sat} (which is essentially ground). One of the flip-flop outputs is taken across the collector load (R18) of Q6 and is in this case ground, or "false" for this particular system.

Also, when Q3 is conducting and Q4 is cut-off, the collector is held at its clamp level of −4.5 V and this potential is coupled through network R6, L1, C2, CR2, and R5 to the base of transistor Q2. Q2 is turned on, and the magnitude of collector current is sufficient to cause approximately ground potential to appear across its collector; this potential is fed through R3 and C1 to the base of output transistor Q1. Q1 is, therefore, cut-off, and the output across its load, R1, is held to the clamp value of −4.5 V by CR1, becoming the X output of the flip-flop (which is the "true" level of voltage for this system).

Since the flip-flop is a symmetrical device, all voltage and current relationships thus analyzed will hold true for the other state (Q3 cut-off and Q4 conducting), except that they will be in inverse order.

Notice that this analysis explains the static condition of the flip-flop; that the output states will not change unless some external force is applied; that these unchanging outputs may represent the indefinite storage of these states; and that the inputs have not yet been considered.

The "set" and "reset" input circuits are comprised of the series of diodes CR12, CR13, CR3, and CR4 and CR14, CR15, CR7, and CR8 in conjunction with CR16 and CR17. The voltage inputs to the "S" and "R" will be logic levels from other flip-flops, pushbuttons, switches, or any circuit capable of logic levels. The inputs to CR16 and CR17 are called *clock-pulses* and are the timing triggers or sync for the computer. There are many flip-flops and other logic devices throughout the computer; hence, some timing is necessary to have the states from each device flow through the machine in an orderly and determinable manner. In the given exemplary system, the clock-pulses are −4.5-V triggers of approximately 0.3-microsecond duration occurring every three microseconds.

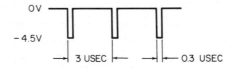

Fig. 6–7. Clock pulses.

The input to the flip-flop under discussion might be from a push-button where the button passes −4.5 V when "pushed," and 0 V or ground, when open. The button may be activated, but no signal should pass into the base of Q3 or Q4 until a clock-pulse occurs. This action is accomplished by the "gate" effect of CR12, CR13, CR3, and CR4 with CR16 because when there is a "true" at the "set" (−4.5 V), CR12 and CR13 are forward-biased and would ordinarily pass the signal through. However, at this time CR16 will have ground potential at its anode and this, in conjunction with −4.5 V passed to its cathode by CR12 and CR13, is sufficient to cause forward-bias, or conduction, hence shorting out the signal, or effectively putting ground between CR13 and CR3. At the

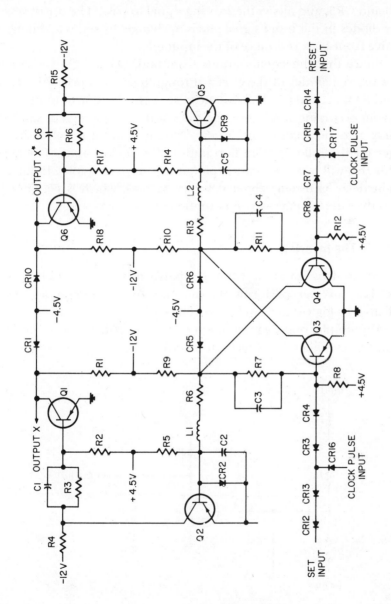

Fig. 6-8. Typical digital flip-flop.

time a clock-pulse (-4.5 V) appears at the anode of CR16, the diode is reverse-biased, cuts off, removes the ground potential from between CR13 and CR3, and allows the existing signal to pass. The use of several series diodes in the input signal line is to change, by series addition, the effective front-back resistance of the input line.

Notice that the signal outputs from both Q3 and Q4 are coupled out to the remainder of the circuit through delay networks R6, L1, and C2 and R13, L2, and C5. This is done to keep the flip-flop outputs (X and X′) from occurring until after the clock-pulse has occurred, since this flip-flop may be feeding the input of another and it is not desired to trigger off the following flip-flop until the next clock-time. The necessity for this will become more apparent in later discussions. In fact, the built-in delay is usually about 0.8 microsecond, which is considerably longer than the 0.3-microsecond duration of the clock-pulses.

6–6 The Inverter

AND and OR gates electronically perform the AND and OR operations. The inverter performs the negation or NOT operation; that is, it will invert a logic signal applied to its input.

Any simple, one-stage common-emitter amplifier inverts the input signal; the amplifier is, in fact, an inverter. Figure 6–9 shows a single-

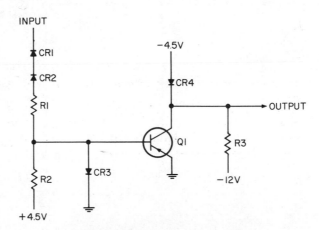

Fig. 6–9. Typical digital inverter circuit.

stage transistor amplifier used as an inverter in a typical digital system. In addition to inversion, the circuit provides current amplification that permits the driving of more gates than the signal at the inverter's input could drive. The example used works in a system using negative voltage for the true state.

During the time the input is in the 0 state (ground potential), CR1 and CR2 are forward-biased through R1 and R2 toward the positive 4.5 V. There is some positive potential drop between R1 and R2 and this positive value is sufficient to cause CR3 to conduct, applying nearly ground potential at the base of Q1. (Actually, owing to the small forward resistance of CR3, there is about +0.7 V at the base of Q1) This reverse bias on Q1 cuts off the transistor, causing the collector to assume the clamp potential of —4.5 V. Hence, a 0 V input produces a —4.5 V output, which is the opposite, or inverted, state. The converse is true when the input is 1 (—4.5 V).

The common logic symbol for an inverter is a circle. For MIL-SPEC drawings, the inverter will be represented by a triangle with internal labeling identifying it as an inverter. The 1 represents the inverter's number and location. Notice that an input A yields an output A^*; input A^* yields output A; and an input AND yields an output OR, and vice versa.

6–7 The Booster

Often it will be necessary to drive logic voltages through many feet of cable between computer units, and often logic voltages produced by a flip-flop, or other devices, may be needed at more gates than the logic-producing circuit is capable of driving. Where these or similar requirements arise, some form of amplification, or boosting, is needed.

The booster does not change the state of the logic signal; it does not perform any logical operation. It supplies the current requirements of succeeding circuits. The inverter provides some amplification but, being a single stage, it complements the input. If two inverters were used in series, the second would recomplement the signal and the logic output would be the same as the original logic input amplified.

$$A = A^*; \qquad A^* = A$$

Essentially, this is exactly what a booster is: two inverters in series. However, it is unnecessary to drive the output of one inverter into another through the diode gating network comprising an inverter's input circuit. To minimize waste, a special second stage called the "gate amplifier" is often used. The input to the gate amplifier requires the entire direct output of an inverter. That is, a booster could be constructed by:

$$\text{inverter} + \text{inverter} = \text{booster}$$

but is usually constructed by:

$$\text{inverter} + \text{gate amplifier} = \text{booster}$$

For some computers, circuits of inverters and gate amplifiers exist separately, and where the logic calls for complementation, inverters are used. Where boosting is required, an inverter plus gate amplifier is used. From a logical standpoint, only inverters and boosters exist, since a gate amplifier is not used by itself.

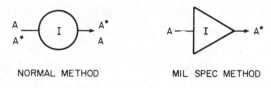

NORMAL METHOD   MIL SPEC METHOD

Fig. 6–10. Inverter logic symbols.

MIL SPEC METHOD

Fig. 6–11. Booster logic symbols.

The booster output is essentially in phase with the input. There is a slight transient delay in passing a signal. The common logical symbol for a booster is a triangle; the MIL-SPEC symbol is also a triangle with identifying letters and often includes a second output for computers that "tap off" from the first stage (inverter).

Figure 6–12 shows a typical inverter and gate amplifier connected to form a booster. Notice that the inverter's output clamping diode is not needed and that the inverter's load resistor (R3, Fig. 6–8) is taken up in the gate-amplifier input circuitry by R18. Negative voltage is considered true for this circuit.

When the input to the booster is 1 (−4.5 V), CR16 and CR17 are shorted, placing some negative potential between R16 and R17 (R17 is much larger than R16). CR18 is cut-off, the base-emitter junction of

Q7 is forward-biased, and very nearly ground potential exists at the collector of Q7. The divider action between R18, R5, and R19 places a positive value on the base of Q8 at this time which is sufficient to cut-off Q8, making its collector assume the clamp value of −4.5 V. This is the same amplified value that is at the input "1," "T," or −4.5 V. Capacitor C4 enhances the switching action and minimizes storage delay of transistor Q8.

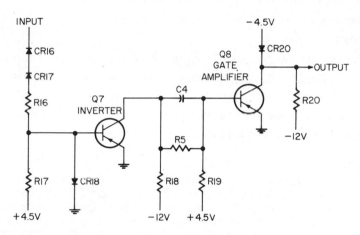

Fig. 6-12. Typical digital booster circuit.

6-8 Conclusion

Points to remember:

(a) Gates (AND and OR), flip-flops, inverters, and boosters perform most of the logic mechanization in computers.

(b) There are several types of flip-flops: JK, RS, KK̄, and others. The RS, in particular, does not allow the condition of both inputs being "true" at the same time. The RS type has become the most common in many current computers, although logic equations will often be seen indicating J as the "set" input and K as the "reset" input with the stipulation that the "1-1" input condition cannot exist. Under these circumstances, it is truly an RS-type flip-flop.

(c) Flip-flop inputs, at any given clock-time, may be in *either* state (except where "1-1" is prohibited), and the outputs at the next clock time will follow the pattern established in the flip-flop truth table. The outputs will *always* represent both states: at one time, if output

X is "false" (0), output X' must be "true," and if output X is "true," X' must be "false."

(d) Flip-flops used as a logic element are purposely designed so that the outputs do not change state until after the input clock-pulse is passed. In the case where, for example, a system's clock-rate is 5 microseconds and the clock-pulse width is 0.5 microseconds, flip-flops in system would be designed to change state around 1.0 to 1.5 μsec after the leading edge of the input clock-pulse had occurred.

(e) Inverters are one-stage amplifiers used to obtain the complement of logic signals.

(f) Boosters are two stages of amplification that may be comprised of two inverters, or of an inverter and gate amplifier connected, providing no logic change, but yielding current amplification.

(g) An example using each of the five basic computer circuits in a strictly hypothetical problem follows.

EXAMPLE:

      Assume three flip-flops FA01–FA03, where A denotes the "activating unit" as the location of these flip-flops (Fig. 6-13). It is desired to light a bank of lamps, which require considerable current, when the push-button controlling flip-flops FA01 AND FA02 is closed OR whenever FA03's button is closed. Assume that these flip-flop outputs are also used elsewhere and, for the sake of illustration, only the leads shown in the diagram are available to light the lamps.

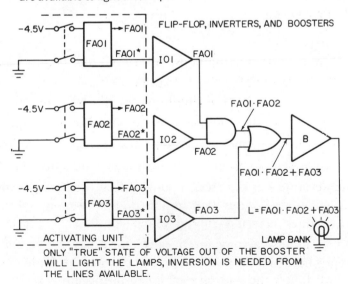

ONLY "TRUE" STATE OF VOLTAGE OUT OF THE BOOSTER WILL LIGHT THE LAMPS, INVERSION IS NEEDED FROM THE LINES AVAILABLE.

Fig. 6–13. Sample logic schematic.

EXERCISES

1. When are the outputs of a multivibrator equal?

2. What is the difference between a JK and an RS flip-flop?

3. The KK flip-flop can accept the 1-1 input condition. (true or false?)

4. The "reset" output of a flip-flop can never be true. (true or false?)

5. Can the flip-flop store a bit of information for longer than a one-bit period of time?

EXERCISES

1. Draw the logic symbol for a JK flip-flop.

2. Complete the following truth for an RS flip-flop.

R	S	Q^n	Q^{n+1}
0	0	0	
0	0	1	
0	1	0	
0	1	1	
1	0	0	
1	0	1	
1	1	0	
1	1	1	

3. What type(s) of flip-flop among those mentioned in the text would be ideally suited for monitoring a single line carrying random input signals.

4. Draw the output waveforms for a JK flip-flop based on the input waveforms shown in Fig. 6–A. Logic levels are defined as true $= -3$ V, false $= 0$ V.

5. What application do inverters and boosters both have in common?

6. What applications do inverters have which boosters do not?

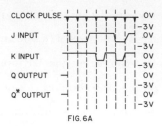

FIG. 6A

7. Complete the waveform portion of Fig. 6B which corresponds to the Q Q* portion. Logic levels are defined as true = 3 V, false = 0 V.

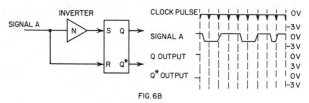

FIG. 6B

8. Given the RS type transistor flip-flop shown in Fig. 6-C with +0 V = true and −V = false. Which input should be marked "S"?

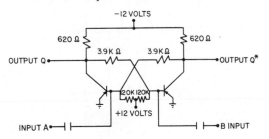

Fig. 6–C

9. Write an AND and OR expression (*f*) for the circuit in Fig. 6-D. (0 V is true and −3 V false.)

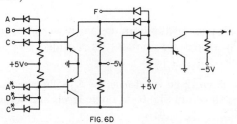

FIG. 6D

7

COMPUTER TERMINOLOGY

7–1 Introduction

Having considered the basic computer circuits (gates, flip-flops, inverters, and boosters), computer language (logical algebra and logic equations), and the system of numbers used by computers (binary), we are ready to consider in more detail the five basic units of computer mechanization:

- Input-Output Unit
- Arithmetic Unit
- Memory Unit
- Control and Timing Unit
- Programming Unit

Although each unit will be studied separately, note that all are interlaced with each other. Since the control and timing unit is scattered throughout the computer, it will be studied last, and understanding its operation will help us understand how the units operate together as a whole.

To avoid interrupting a circuit description to explain a basic computer term, a brief list of common computer terminology follows.

7-2 Clock-Pulse

This is the timing trigger, or sync-pulse, for computer operations. Clock-pulses are evenly spaced triggers with the same polarity as that selected for the "true" state. The frequency of these pulses is a function of the original design requirements.

7-3 Counters

The counter, as the name implies, counts signals fed to its input. Counters, like the clock-pulse, are often used to provide timing. For example, it might be desired to have a gate open at every fourth clock-pulse only. A counter would be provided that counts four clock-pulses, and at count four supplies a pulse output. This provides a measure of real time, since each clock-pulse occurs at a discrete interval of time.

7-4 Bit

Bit is an abbreviation of BInary digiT. Bits are the time, or space, between clock-pulses. That is, one "bit-time" is the time between the leading edge of one CP (clock-pulse) and the leading edge of the next CP. A bit describes a single character in the logic language. For example, the binary number 101 has three bits. Bits can be true or false.

7-5 MSD, LSD

For the binary number 101, the bit at the far left is the *most significant digit* (MSD). It is $1 \times 2^2 = 4$; hence it carries the most "weight" in the number. The bit at the far right is $1 \times 2^0 = 1$, which carries the least weight in the number; hence this bit is the *least significant digit* (LSD). Often MSD is called MSB (most significant bit), and LSD is called LSB (least significant bit).

7-6 Word

A *word* is a number of bits representing some desired information For example, the binary number 11010 has five bits. This is a five-bit word for the decimal number 26. A word indicating a target's height might require 30 bits. The word length (number of bits) used in any given computer is determined by the design requirements.

7-7 Format

The bits in a "word" must be arranged in an orderly manner. This is done according to the word format. For example, a 30-bit height word might be arranged according to the following format (counting from right to left):

First five bits hold the target number.
Next four bits hold a possible break-up of height into sectors (0–5,000; 5,000–10,000; 10,000–20,000; 20,000–50,000 feet.)
Next 15 bits hold the actual height.
The last six bits could be spares for future information.

7-8 Address

An address is an expression, usually numerical, that designates a particular location or destination of information. For instance, since words are stored in the computer memory unit, part of the word format must include an "address" for the word. This provides a method of finding the word at any time.

7-9 Parallel and Serial Operation

Parallel operation of a computer pertains to simultaneous transmission of, storage of, or logical operations on, information. For example, parallel removal of a word from storage would mean taking all bits out at the same time (one clock-pulse). This requires a line for each bit of the word. Serial operation pertains to step-by-step (clock-pulse-to-clock-pulse) transmission of, storage of, or logical operation on information. For example, serial removal of a word from storage would mean starting with bit one and taking each bit out clock-pulse by clock-pulse. This requires only one line for the entire word.

7-10 Memory

Memory is a device to retain information for later withdrawal; often called store, or storage. There are many devices that can store the "true" or "false" states. Flip-flops, at any given time, are storing information; switches are "open" or "closed." Magnetic material, magnetized in one direction for "true," and in the other for "false," could be used as a memory device.

Memory devices fall into two classes: (a) volatile, (b) permanent. A *volatile* store is a device that loses its information with an interruption of power, or after a period of time. Examples are:

flip-flops
cathode-ray tubes
delay lines
relays

A *permanent* store retains its information, regardless of power loss or the passage of time. Examples are:

magnetic tapes
magnetic cores
magnetic drums
manual switches

7–11 Register

Register is a device capable of retaining information; usually it is a buffer between the main memory and the other units. Often it holds, temporarily, one word or a message containing many words. Registers are usually made of flip-flops or magnetic cores, and characteristically contain as many flip-flops or cores as there are bits in the word to be stored. For example, an input register, comprised of flip-flops, might be loaded by switches that an operator manipulates according to a format he has just written. After this slow, manual loading of the register, a button, (typically marked "enter,") being depressed would allow the contents of the register to pour out (either serially or in parallel) into the main memory at the normal computer CP rate. As another example, two height words on two different targets might need to be compared. These words could be called up by their addresses, pulled out of the main memory, and loaded into two temporary registers. After comparison, the two words would leave the temporary registers and be re-entered (by addresses) into the main memory.

7–12 Access Time

Access time is a time interval that is characteristic of a storage unit; essentially it is a measure of the time required to communicate with that unit. For example, if a magnetic tape were being used as the main memory and the tape were traveling between the pickup heads in a long, continuous loop, and it were desired to check a certain word at address 64, it would be necessary to wait until this word passed between the pickup heads. Of course, if at the start of this search for word 64 the tape was at word 63, the waiting period would be short; hence, we would have a fast access time. But the tape might have been at word 65, in which case the waiting period would be long. Usually the access time for a memory is considered to be the maximum time required to find information.

7-13 Read, Write

To *read* is to take information from a store. To *write* is to place information in the store.

7-14 Clear

To *clear* restore a storage device to a prescribed state, usually that denoting zero, or to reset the device to zero.

7-15 Matrix, Encoding, Decoding

The *matrix*, when used in digital function, is any logical network whose configuration is a rectangular array of intersections of input-output leads. Often the word is loosely used to describe symmetrical arrays of elements. In the description of digital functions, *encoding* is the process of changing information from any form to digital form, and *decoding* is the changing of digital information to some other form. Encoding networks generally excite only one input and produce a combination of outputs, while decoding changes a combination of inputs to one output. These "encoding-decoding" operations are performed in symmetrical arrays, and are, hence, loosely called "matrix" devices.

7-16 Program

The *program* is a prepared routine; a plan by which the computer proceeds to solve problems. For example, suppose it were desired to have a general-purpose computer solve:

$$X^2 + 2X + 4 = ?$$

When the selected numerical values for the variable(s) of the equation have been stored in the computer, a person called the "programmer" next writes out a series of steps, or orders, that the computer must follow to solve this problem. These orders would control the computer through the "input unit," or through the "programmer unit" if one is provided for the given computer.

(1) Take X from the main store to the arithmetic unit.

(2) Multiply X times X

(3) Place product (X^2) back in store.

(4) Take X from main store to arithmetic unit.

(5) Add X to X.

(6) Place sum back in store.

(7) Take X^2 from store to temporary storage register.

(8) Take $2X$ from store to arithmetic unit.

(9) Add $2X$ to contents of temporary storage register.

(10) Place sum back in temporary store.

(11) Take number 4 from store to arithmetic unit.

(12) Add number 4 to contents of temporary register.

(13) Place sum in output register B.

Both general-purpose and special-purpose computers will have program routines, similar to the foregoing example, written out by programmers. Once the program has proven acceptable in the special-purpose computer, it will be inserted into the machine (wired-in) and never changed. However, the program must change for every changing problem that the general-purpose computer may be expected to solve.

The foregoing example represents only the principle of the steps involved in programming. Actual programming is more detailed, containing addresses, conditionalities, and so on.

Most of these "computer terms" will be covered in later sections, and the others will become familiar by repeated use in context.

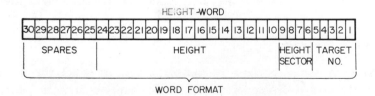

Fig. 7–1. Sample line format.

8

MEMORY UNIT

8-1 Defining a Memory

Any computing device must have a *memory*. The common action of using pencil and paper when solving mathematical problems provides memory. Pressing the keys of an adding machine to enter the values of a problem into the machine causes the values to be remembered until the lever is pulled or the button is pressed that tells the machine to add the remembered values.

With modern computers performing such a wide variety of tasks, a great number of the components that make up the computer are memory devices. Any electrical or mechanical element that can maintain a stable state until called on to deliver its information can be used as a memory device. For digital computers, any element that can represent true or false values is a memory device. A number of memory devices that, when grouped together, hold a desired amount of information are generally referred to as a *register*. These storage registers are distributed throughout a large computer and perform the function (as does a pencil and paper) of holding information for any given length of time. Since a great many data must be held, or remembered, it is customary to provide an area in the computer known as the *main memory*, or *main store*. The

107

main memory in a digital computer is one of the important elements that sets the computer above the desk calculator. The calculator has memory capability that usually exists from one problem to the next, whereas the main memory of a digital computer may hold a great many data for an indefinite period of time, regardless of how many times the information is used in any problem. This characteristic, in fact, makes the computer similar to the human brain, which also stores indefinitely all facts it has learned. The difference here is that the information may be hard to recall from the human brain, whereas it has been electrically stored in a computer's memory and it is electrically recallable (barring a complete loss of power).

Memory devices are divided into two classes: volatile and permanent. A *volatile* memory device is one that loses its stored data if the device loses its power source, or after a certain amount of time passes. On the other hand, a *permanent* memory device retains its stored data despite a power failure or the infinite passage of time.

The more common memory devices used in modern computers are flip-flops for temporary (volatile) registers, and some form of magnetic device for the main (permanent) store.

8-2 Permanent Storage

The two magnetic devices most commonly used in computers are the magnetic tape (or some form thereof) and the core matrix. Each has certain advantages and disadvantages, which will be discussed in the sections that follow.

8-3 Tape Memory

In the process of developing types of permanent magnetic storage devices, early efforts used the straightforward and available magnetic tape. Magnetizing the tape under the recording (write) head with flux in one direction might represent true, while magnetizing in the opposite direction would represent false. A serial train of binary information can be impressed on the tape as it is driven past the write head. Driving the tape past a play-back head allows the same information to be picked up, or read out. As with ordinary tape recorders, the same head can be used for writing and reading as long as it is not used for both at the same time. The problem with tapes is that they are ordinarily kept on feed and take-up spools, and if it is desired to read what has just been written, one of the following must occur:

(a) The tape must be reversed, driven back past the recorded data, and driven forward again with the head set to read.

(b) The tape must be completely wound onto the take-up spool and this spool be interchanged with the feed spool; then the tape must be started through with the head set to read.

Where time is no problem, these methods can be useful. There is another method of access in which there is one long loop with no feed or take-up spools. When this method is used, all that is necessary to read what has just been written is to set the head for read and wait for the tape to transverse the loop. However, there are disadvantages to this method, for if it were necessary to store a great quantity of data, the tape would be uncommonly long. Of course, the longer the loop, the more complex must the idler-wheel mechanism needed to hold the tape. Even though the long tape loop has many inherent problems, it is possible to record more than one channel of binary data on a single tape using multiwound heads; hence, it is possible to store a great deal of information on one tape loop. While the inherently long access time of magnetic tape does not allow it to be used for the main, high-speed memory of modern digital computers, tape does serve well as the external memory device providing permanent, large-capacity storage for constants and related functions that may be needed infrequently in the main computer.

8-4 The Core Memory

Another device that can be used for permanent, magnetic storage is the ferrite core. The core is a ring of magnetic (ferrite) material. As with tapes, the condition of storing true and false data is magnetization in one direction for true and in the other direction for false.

Magnetic material is ideal for permanent storage. Ferrite cores, for instance, can be magnetized easily and rapidly by small electrical currents. Moreover, there are two directions of magnetization; hence, the storage of two logical states is possible. High-quality magnetic materials do not lose information when electrical power is lost and the passage of time does not measurably affect the magnetic properties of the substance (either the flux density or its direction). In fact, it takes some positive force, or action, to redirect the magnetization. For permanent storage in digital computers it is desirable to use a magnetic

material having a high remanent flux density and a nearly rectangular
hysteresis loop to assure permanent magnetization over long periods of
time. These properties are attained with many special magnetic alloys.
Among them are the ferrites formed by molding and heating a raw
magnetic alloy that is originally in a powder form. Eddy currents are
then small because the individual particles in the ferrite are insulated
from each other through the use of a suitable binder in the molding
and heating operations. Figure 8–1A shows a core (toroid) with a single
winding, and Figs. 8–1B and 8–1C show the possible hysteresis loops
that might accompany this core of magnetic material.

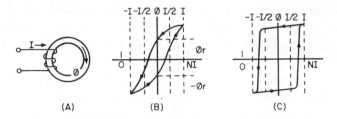

Fig. 8–1. Sample core and hysteresis loops.

The quantity of flux, ϕ, existing in the core is a function of the
amp-turns (NI) or mmf (magnetomotive force) applied to the core winding at any given time. Since, in this illustration, the coil turns, N, will
not change, it will be easier to neglect N and think of the flux as a
function only of current in the winding. At any time that the winding
current, I, is zero, there is some remanent flux, $\pm\phi_r$, in the core, depending on the core's previous state. If "true," or one, is arbitrarily selected
as $+\phi$ and it is desired to change the core state to false (zero) when the
core has $+\phi_r$ remanent flux, then it will take some current, $-I$, in the
winding to produce this change. Notice that if the core has a non-
rectangular hysteresis loop (Fig. 8–1B), a current $-I/2$ would bring ϕ
down near zero, or place the core in an indeterminate state, whereas
if the core has a rectangular hysteresis loop, $-I/2$ does not change ϕ
significantly (Fig. 8–1C). This is an important characteristic of the more
rectangular loop, and it makes a rectangular loop necessary for storage
of logic states. This will become more apparent later.

When ferrite cores are used as a computer's main memory they
are usually arranged in an orderly matrix as shown in Fig. 8–2A. In this
diagram, there are four cores in the x plane and four in the y and hence
16 cores, or 16 distinct places for individual bits to be stored. Notice

that there are four separate excitation wires in the x plane (A, B, C, D) and four in the y plane (N–Q), and one readout, or sense wire, that passes through each core. Any individual core is defined by its x and y excitation wires, i.e., its x and y "address." Core BP is shown shaded.

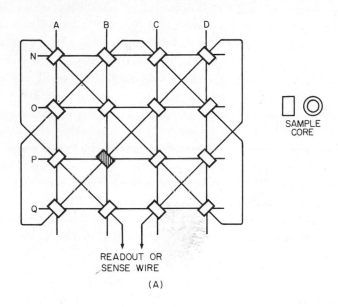

(A)

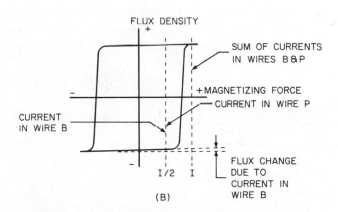

(B)

Fig. 8-2. Sample core layout and hysteresis loop.

8-5 Writing

If core BP happens to be in the 0 state ($-\phi_r$ residual flux) and it is desired to change it to the 1 state, it will take a combination of current from wire B and wire P to accomplish the $+\phi$ condition. That is, the excitation current in wire B is of the $I/2$ magnitude (from the example of Fig. 8–1) and is not sufficient to change significantly the existing $-\phi_r$ flux in core BP (see hysteresis loop, Fig. 8–2B), but, when current in wire P of magnitude $I/2$ and flowing in the *same* direction as current B also passes through core BP, the sum of B and P is I and this is sufficient current to cause core BP's flux to move up to $+\phi$, or the 1 state; therefore, the current in wire B had no effect on cores BN, BO, or BQ, nor did the current in wire P have any effect on cores PA, PC, or PD since each of these cores had only $I/2$ excitation current. Only core BP had $I/2 + I/2 = I$ excitation current. Of course, had core BP been in the 1 state and had it been desired to write a 1 on the core, no actual change would have taken place when currents B and P occurred. The core was already 1 and it would stay 1. It must also be realized that the winding of wire B and P around core BP must be such that when the excitation currents in these wires are supposed to be writing a 1, the inductive action between the two windings is additive. All assumptions as to which flux condition represented 1 could be reversed and the same theory of writing would hold.

8–6 Reading

Investigating Fig. 8–3, we notice that when the core is in the 1 state (flux arbitrarily clockwise), and for the continued length of time it remains in the 1 state, there is no current in the sense winding because

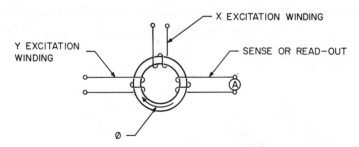

Fig. 8–3. Read-write technique in cores.

there is no changing field. However, when the 1 was initially written onto this core (assuming it was originally demagnetized), the sharply rising flux in the clockwise direction did cause a current, for a short period, in the sense winding. But this was the "writing period" and the current pulse that existed in the sense winding at this time was not needed. What is needed is a way to sense, or read, the magnetized state of the core at some later time. By actually rewriting with 1's or 0's and calling this period, or the time, "read cycle," this can be accomplished. That is, suppose it is desired to read the state of the core in Fig. 8–3 five minutes after it was originally forced into the 1 state. If 1s are used for *reading*, then the proper magnitude of currents in the x and y windings to cause a 1 condition would be applied to the core, and the action that takes place in the sense winding would indicate what condition the core has been in for the last five minutes. Since a 1 already exists in the core, application of another 1 would have no effect in the sense winding, but this is indication enough that a 1 exists in the core. Had the core been in the 0 state and if a 1 *read* pulse were applied, the core would change state and a current pulse would occur in the sense winding. Therefore, when a 1 read pulse is used, no sense current indicates the core was 1; a sense-current pulse indicates the core was 0. Of course, if a 0 read pulse is used, then the opposite effects indicate a core's previous condition.

Notice carefully:

(a) It must be known whether a "read period" or "write period" is taking place, since excitation currents of the same magnitude are used for both cycles.

(b) Reading may be accomplished with either a 1 pulse or a 0 pulse. Once the choice has been made, any given computer, using core matrices, will consistently use only one read pulse type.

(c) The process of reading might be *destructive*. That is, whenever a 1 pulse read cycle is used and a core happens to be in the 0 state, the core will be changed to a 1 as it is read. It is desirable simply to "read" the core and not destroy the state it is in; therefore, core memories make provisions to rewrite immediately after a read cycle.

8–7 Core Matrix Layout

The core memory lends itself particularly well to parallel operation; i.e., each bit of a word is read out at the same time (in parallel). It is customary to provide a core plane for each bit of a word. If a system uses 10-bit words, there would be 10 core planes in the main memory. Figure 8–4 shows a layout for a three-bit word system. The number of cores in the x axis times the number in the y axis of the diagram define the word capacity of the matrix. The illustration shows how the cores might appear holding the binary word 101. Notice that the excitation wires are along the x and y axes and the sense wires are along the z plane.

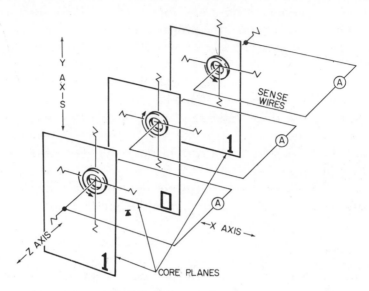

Fig. 8-4. Core memory layout.

For a particular method of using a core matrix, consider the following example. Assume that the core planes consist of an 8×8 array and each word contains 30 bits. Figure 8-5A shows only a single plane, but since the operation for each plane is identical, only the one plane need be explained. However, it must be understood that there is a total of 30 planes along the z axis. In addition to the x and y drive lines, sense and inhibit lines pass through each core. The inhibit line is parallel to the x drive line but would provide the same function if it were parallel to the y drive line. Figure 8-5B shows the wires passing through a single core. A particular core is addressed by passing a current pulse of $I/2$ amplitude through both the x and y lines of the selected core. In this way, the selected core (core A) receives the full-amplitude pulse and the other cores on the same x and y lines (cores B and C) receive half-amplitude pulses and are called *half-selected*. All the remaining cores (cores D and E) are termed *unselected*.

Binary information stored in a core is determined by the polarity of its remanent magnetization and is extracted by pulsing each of the drive lines. In the preceding example, the read pulse is such that the core is magnetized in the 0 condition. If the core is storing a 1, the flux change will induce a voltage in the sense winding. If no voltage is induced in the sense winding this indicates that the core was in the 0 state.

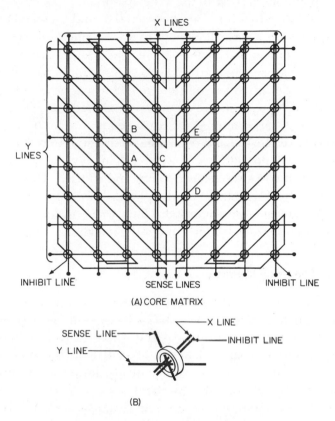

Fig. 8–5. Typical core plane arrangement.

When a core is being selected, a read pulse is followed by a write pulse of opposite polarity on the drive lines. (For this reason, the drive lines are also called read/write lines.) The write pulse will be of such a polarity as to leave the selected core in the 1 state. If it is desired to leave a 0 in the selected core, an inhibiting pulse, opposite in polarity to the write pulse, is supplied simultaneously with the write pulse. The inhibit pulse will partially cancel the effect of the write pulse leaving the core in the 0 state.

Since the read process is destructive, each read operation must be followed by the write operation if the information is to remain in the memory. Therefore, as an example, the reading process might be used to set an external 30-bit flip-flop register to the state of the 30-bit stored word. The state of each flip-flop could then be used to determine the need for an inhibiting pulse in the write operation.

Typical individual cores are between 0.05 and 0.4 inch in diameter. Some special cores are small enough to fit on a pin head. With many of the special magnetic materials it is not necessary to actually wind the excitation and sense wires around the cores; simply passing the wires through the cores provides sufficient mmf for magnetization. Common core memories range in size from approximately 20,000 to 200,000-bit capacities. A large number of cores require large driving currents and extensive read-write and recirculation circuitry, but cores are stable and rugged and provide very fast access to stored data. The access time for typical cores ranges between 5 and 15 μsec. The access into a core memory bank is called "random access' since *any* bit, or word, of data can be taken at any asynchronous time, whereas a tape, for example, must take a datum when it comes under the read head.

8–8 The Drum Memory

Another form of permanent magnetic storage is the magnetic drum. Essentially, the drum is a stack of magnetic tapes. It is a metal cylinder that revolves about its axis and whose surface is coated with a magnetic material. Logical data are recorded on the surface of this drum in practically the same manner in which they are recorded on a tape. Owing to its physical design, the drum combines some of the advantages of both tapes and cores. The drum is divided into channels along its axis, and each channel is divided into sectors. Each channel is like one magnetic tape. There will be a read and/or write head for each channel and sometimes more than one read/write head per channel. In this respect, the drum is like dozens of tapes running at the same time and at the same speed, but the drum is not constructed for fragile tapes and makes one revolution in a very short time (typically, in the neighborhood of 30 msec. for one revolution). The drum is characteristically a serial storage device, but where fast access to data is necessary, each bit of a word can be recorded on a different channel and be simultaneously written or read by a head for each bit. (See Fig. 8–6.)

Drums have been constructed with diameters ranging from two inches to four feet and with lengths ranging from about one inch to three feet. Typical drums are between six to twelve inches in radius and approximately ten to sixteen inches along their axis. Along a

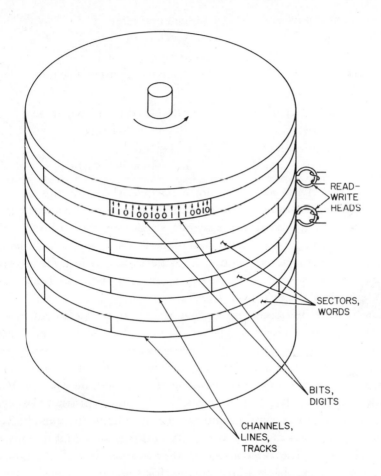

READ–
WRITE
HEADS

SECTORS,
WORDS

BITS,
DIGITS

CHANNELS,
LINES,
TRACKS

TOTAL BITS=BITS/INCH X TOTAL CIRCUMFERENCE
(IN INCHES) X NO. OF CHANNELS

Fig. 8–6. Drum layout.

channel (sometimes called a "line" or "track"), the recording density is usually between 50 to 150 bits per inch. The number of channels per axial length is limited by physical head dimensions and the point where magnetic flux from one channel begins to interfere with the adjacent channel. Typical values are from 15 to 30 channels per inch of drum length. The storage capacity of an average-size drum might be found as follows:

Given:

drum dimensions	12-inch diameter
	8-inch length
	20 channels per axial inch
record density	50 bits per circumference inch

Solution:

circumference	$\pi d = (3.14)(12) = 37.6$ inches
total bits per channel	$(37.6)(50) = 1890$ bits
total number of channels	$(20)(8) = 160$
total storage capacity	$(160)(1890) = 302{,}000$ bits

Notice that this drum (which is not a particularly large one, nor is it using a high record density) provides a great deal of storage capacity. Figure 8-6 shows a typical drum layout. The sector, which breaks up a channel, is merely a logical subdivision of data. A sector may include only one word or it may include all the words necessary to describe a certain condition. For some computers using drum memories, the breakdown within channels is simply called "words."

The read/write heads may or may not make physical contact with the drum surface. Where a surface-contacting head is used, higher record densities are usually realized along with a steadier level of output data, but there is some wear problem and usually considerable associated "noise." Where noncontact heads are used, no wear problem and little associated "head noise" exist, but the gap adjustment between head and drum can be critical, and the drum dimensions must be very accurate. Also, generally, record density and output-signal magnitude are reduced when the noncontact head is compared with the contact head. Unlike cores, the reading process for both drums and tapes is nondestructive. The realtive motion between drum and head provides the necessary changing field effect.

8-9 Read Write Techniques for Drums

The same pulses of current that suffice for cores are not the most desirable for writing on drums. A typical configuration for a read/write head is shown in Fig. 8-7A. When the magnetic head is placed with its gap close to the magnetic surface of the drum, the lines of flux will tend to pass through the "low-resistance" magnetic material on the surface instead of across the "high-resistance" air gap, resulting in a magnetized region on the drum surface. When the head is removed

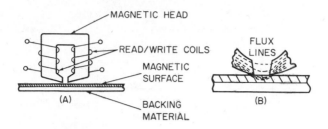

Fig. 8–7. Write technique on drums.

from the area, the magnetized region of the surface is similar to a small bar magnet with the lines of flux returning through the air from one end of the bar to the other. If the head is returned to the same position, the flux lines from the surface will tend to pass through the low-reluctance path provided by the magnetic head instead of through the air. Figure 8–7B shows this storage process more clearly. The development, or change, of flux lines in the head is greatest when the current to the head windings is undergoing a change. Suppose the binary number 100110 is to be written on the drum surface. Figure 8–8A shows the current pulses in the head windings. (Each column represents one-bit time.) Since the maximum rate of current change is between 1s and 0s, it is at these times that the maximum flux will be induced into the magnetic surface, and it is also at these times that the subsequent passage of a read head would develop a maximum output voltage (Fig. 8–8B). A long *string* of 0s or 1s tends to look like one long 0 or one long 1.

It is possible to decipher signals that are written this way by incorporating timing circuits that "look" for the next 1 or 0 after a long string of either, but it is much more convenient to provide a writing technique that causes some positive action in the center of each bit time. This is accomplished by changing the phase of the writing-current pulse in the middle of a bit time. This method, variously known as "double pulse," or "phase" modulation, or more commonly "Ferranti logic," is shown in Fig. 8–8D.

Notice that the voltage readout has a peak near the center of each bit time whether a string of 1s or 0s occurs or not. As with all logic, the choice of polarities is arbitrary, but there is still a distinct, 180-degree difference between the 1 and 0 readout.

To produce Ferranti logic, the normal steady-state logic to be stored must be changed to an alternating or fluctuating state before

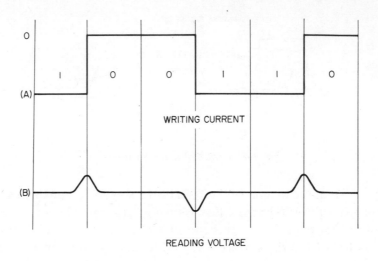

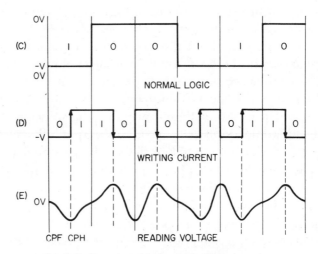

Fig. 8-8. Drum read-write wave shapes.

reaching the write head (Fig. 8-8D). This is done in a special "write flip-flop" and amplifier. A good example of a write flip-flop is shown in Fig. 8-9. The key to this system is a clock-pulse, produced halfway between the main clock-pulses, called the "half clock" (CP$_H$). This half clock occurs at the same frequency as the main clock but is displaced

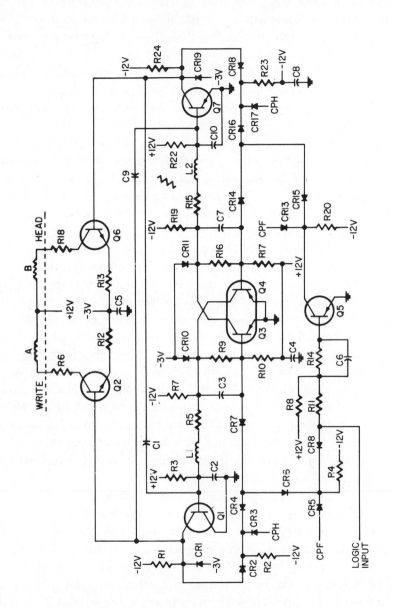

Fig. 8-9. Simplified write flip-flop and write amplifier.

180 degrees. The operation of the write flip-flop is similar to the high-current flip-flop (previous example) with the exception of the input gating and inverter (Q5). Inverter Q5 permits operation of the flip-flop with only one logic input (see $K\overline{K}$ flip-flop) as opposed to the two logic inputs of the high-current flip-flop. Considering first the full-time clock-pulse (CP_F) gates and neglecting the half-time gates, we can see that the logical input is "ANDed" with CP_F at the base of Q3, while the negation of the logical input is "ANDed" with CP_F at the base of Q4. This ensures that both switching transistors (Q3 and Q4) cannot be triggered simultaneously; i.e., a true input (−4.5 V) will turn on Q3 (at CP_F time), while the negation of this −4.5 V will turn off Q4. A "false" input will turn off Q3 because of the slight positive potential at its base, while the negation of the false input will turn on Q4.

The two outputs of Q3 and Q4 drive through delay networks to the base of Q1 and Q7. The collector outputs of these stages are split, with part of the signal going to the base of the write amplifier stages (Q2 and Q6), while part is fed back through CR2 and CR18 toward the base of Q3 and Q4. Because of the delay, the signal fed back cannot appear at Q3 and Q4 until after the CP_F has occurred. More important is the fact that when a "true" signal is fed back (and this is the polarity of signal that will have an active influence on either Q3 or Q4) the CP_H gates (CR3 and CR17) short this signal out except when CP_H occurs. This is the same gating scheme employed at the inputs to the high-current flip-flop. When a half clock-pulse occurs, either Q3 or Q4 changes state, depending on which is conducting and which is cut-off. For instance, if Q3 is set into conduction at CP_F, Q4 will be cut-off, Q1 will subsequently conduct, and Q7 will subsequently cut-off. This causes a "true" level to feed back from Q7, and a "false" level from Q1. At CP_H, the "true" level from Q7 passes to the base of Q4 (which was cut-off), causing this transistor to conduct and Q3 to cut-off. The flip-flop has "flipped" in the middle of the bit time. It follows, then, that during any one bit time (from CP_F to CP_F) there is alternately current in one head winding and then the other, as provided by the amplifiers Q2 and Q6. One head winding will cause magnetization on the drum surface in one direction during the first half of a bit time, while the other head winding will cause magnetization in the other direction during the second half of a bit time. This effectively places a sine wave of flux on the drum as it passes beneath the head; the polarity of this wave depends on which head winding conducted first, which depends on whether a 1 or 0 is being written.

The read voltage (Fig. 8–8E) is amplified and clipped in the read amplifier and ideally appears as shown in Fig. 8–11C. This signal must be coverted back into normal logic. There are many methods for accomplishing this; one would be to gate the read amplifier output (Fig. 8–11C) with a half clock-pulse (Fig. 8–11D) into a flip-flop yielding normal logic (Fig. 8–11E), which is now delayed by 1/2 clock time. This much delay is inconvenient, but when this signal (Fig. 8–11E) is fed into another flip-flop that is gated with a normal clock-pulse, it will be delayed another half clock time and hence a total of one clock time, which could be taken into consideration as far as the rest of the computer is concerned. Notice that these "read peaks" occurred exactly at half clock times because Figs. 8–8 and 8–11 assumed the same head, unmoved, was used both to read and to write. Ordinarily, most drum channels have separate read/ write heads with a certain specified number of data to be stored between heads. The separate *read* head will be adjusted to pick up a peak that was produced at CP_H as far as the *write* head is concerned, but which is simply a voltage peak as far as the read head can tell, since the read head is not connected, in a synchronous manner, with the stationary write head. This is shown in Fig. 8–10. If the voltage picked up by this read

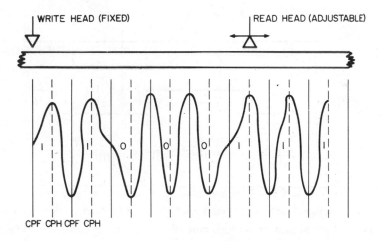

(THERE ARE SEVEN BITS STORED BETWEEN THESE HEADS, AS ADJUSTED)

Fig. 8–10. Flux wave and adjustable read head.

head is amplified and shaped and then gated with a main clock-pulse, it will appear exactly the same as the original logic with no half clock time delay.

For example, a typical read amplifier that can be used is shown in Fig. 8–12. For this circuit, the read head is adjusted to pick up the peaks

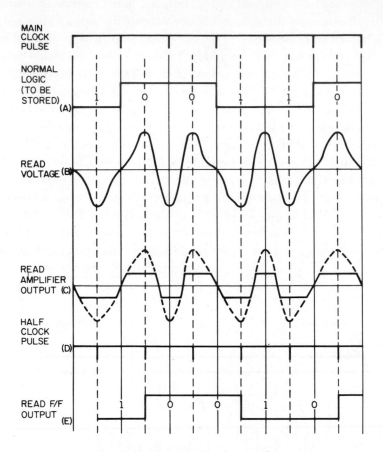

Fig 8–11. Drum read cycle waveshapes.

that were written at CP_H. The first stage is a Class A amplifier driving T1. The center-tapped secondary drives Q2 and Q3 that make up a push-pull stage. The signal polarities out of T1 cause Q2 and Q3 to be conducting alternately; hence, there are two signals, 180 degrees out of phase, at TP2 and TP3. Notice that these two signals are gated with full-time clock-pulses in the AND gates comprised of CR2, CR3, and R5 and CR4, CR5, and R6. The gate outputs are fed to the "set" and "reset" inputs of a read flip-flop.

Figure 8–13 shows a composite of action occurring in a complete write-read cycle.

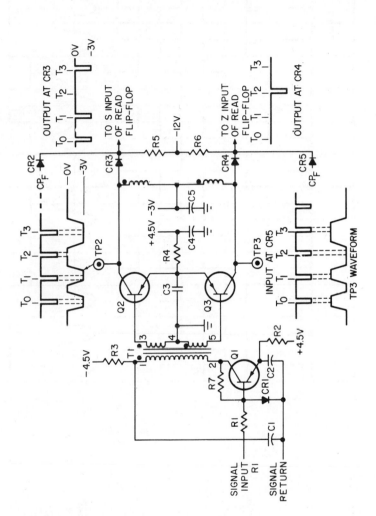

Fig. 8-12. Simplified read amplifier.

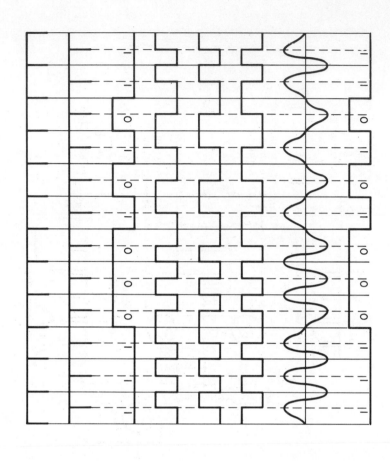

Fig. 8-13. Composite read-write waveshapes.

CLOCK PULSE FULL

CLOCK PULSE HALF

INPUT (NORMAL LOGIC)

WRITE FLIP-FLOP
(FERRANTI) OUTPUT

WRITE AMPLIFIER
WINDING A

WRITE AMPLIFIER
WINDING B

E READ HEAD
(INPUT TO READ AMPLIFIER)

OUTPUT OF READ
FLIP-FLOP

8-10 Registers

A *register* (see Sec. 7-11) is "a device capable of retaining information; usually it is a buffer between the main memory and the other units. Often it holds, temporarily, one word of a message containing many words." Most computers use flip-flops for registers, and usually one register has as many flip-flops as there are bits in a word. However, any of the memory devices can be used to construct a register. The fact that most registers are used as a temporary storage location does not mean that the stored information must be read out before a certain passage of time or be lost; it simply means that a register is usually used to hold data for a few moments before they pass on. Barring power failures, a flip-flop register will hold data indefinitely.

Registers may be loaded serially or in parallel and the information may be transferred out serially or in parallel. Any given register can be mechanized in any one of the four possible input/output configurations.

Input	*Output*
Serial ——————————→	Serial
Serial ——————————→	Parallel
Parallel ——————————→	Serial
Parallel ——————————→	Parallel

As an example, consider the serial transfer of data through a four-flip-flop register shown in Fig. 8-14. (Remember, at the time data

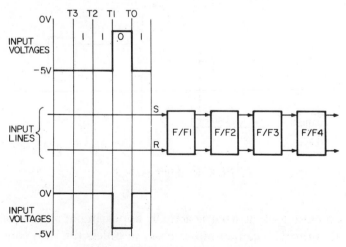

Fig. 8-14. Serial data shift register.

and a CP occur at a flip-flop's input, the output assumes a certain configuration depending on what the input is, but this output does not take
place until after the CP has ceased.) Neglecting the source of data,
assume that the binary number 1011 is presented serially on the input
lines. The LSD comes along at some clock time, T_0, the next digit at T_1,
the next at T_2, etc. Assuming all flip-flops are in the "reset" state before
the data are applied, the pulse at T_0, sets F1. At T_1, F1 is "reset" and F2 is
"set" by the output of F1. At T_2, F1 is "set," F2 is "reset" by F1's output,
and F3 is "set" by F2's output. Finally, at T_3, F1 is left in the "set" state,
F2 is "set" by F1's output, F3 is "reset" by F2's output, and F4 is "set" by
F3's output. At this time, the flip-flops (F1–F4) are consecutively in 1101
states. Notice that each input-state has marched serially down the chain
of flip-flops. When they are all loaded, the output could be taken from
each flip-flop in parallel (in one bit time) at any later time, or the output
could be taken from F4 serially (which would, of course, take four bit
times). Conversely, the flip-flops could be loaded in parallel and would,
therefore, assume their loaded states in one bit time and then be "read,"
at some later time, either serially or in parallel. It is common practice to
draw a logic circuit in the simplified manner shown in Fig. 8–14, where it
is simply understood that clock-pulses are also part of the inputs of these
flip-flops. It may also be noticed that some "shifting" or "loading" control logic would also have to be applied at the inputs, or else nothing
would stop the input data from marching in and right on out. Figure 8–15

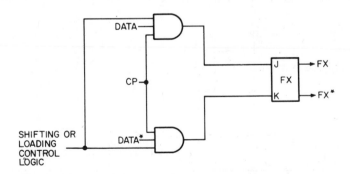

Fig. 8–15. Shift methods.

gives us a close look at what is actually appearing at a register's input.
We see that the data cannot move in or out unless the shift control logic
is present (true).

8-11 Core Shift Register

Magnetic cores may also be used to produce shift registers, although many factors must be considered. The following discussion pertains to the type of core register used in a recent tactical data computer. Although the discussion is not general, it does give the reader a typical method.

There are two modes of operation in core registers: "continuous shifting" and "on-off." In the "continuous shifting" mode, the register operates simply as a delay element, the information becoming available at the output as many bit times after it is entered at the input as there are cores in the register. In other words, the register holds 10 bits, it delays the output by 10 bit times. The "on-off" mode refers to the additional capability of the register to be logically gated off, with a certain number of bits being stored, until the register is again turned on. The core register is composed of five different types of circuits: input circuit, internal register modules, output circuit, magnetic-core shift-register flip-flop, and a driver circuit (Fig. 8-16). The input circuit transforms the computer logic signals to pulse signals that are used throughout the register. The internal register modules each store one

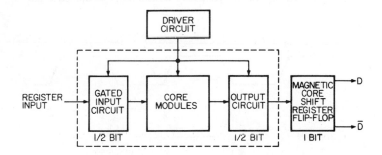

Fig. 8-16. Block diagram of core shift register.

bit of information in a two-core-per-bit configuration. The output circuit converts the current-pulse signals to the register into suitable trigger signals for the shift-register flip-flop, which restores the information to the DC level logic signals. The driver circuit generates the current pulses used in shifting the information through the modules.

Cores used in a shift register are of the same type and have the same rectangular hysteresis loop as those used in a core main memory. It takes a given quantity of current (which may be the sum of more than one current source) to change the state of "rectangural loop" materials.

More important, currents of less than this given value do not noticeably affect the materials' given state.

Since control and timing are important to a shift register, the control "times" and "pulses" are defined as follows:

(a) The time from a full-time clock-pulse to the next half-time clock-pulse is considered α(alpha) time, and

(b) The time from a half-time clock to the next full-time clock is considered β(beta) time.

(c) These times are represented by current pulses I_α and I_β generated by the driver circuit.

These time and control pulses are shown in Fig. 8–17.

Further definition must be made concerning the output flip-flop of the core register. The type of flip-flop used is called an *override flip-flop*. The override flip-flop is similar to those previously discussed with

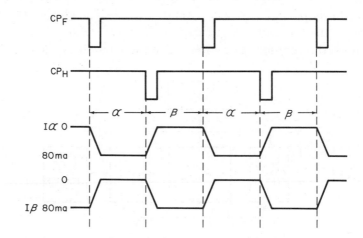

Fig. 8–17. Driver circuit timing.

the exception that a true condition is allowed on *both* inputs. When *both inputs become true*, the *set side overrides the reset side* and the flip-flop becomes set—hence the term override flip-flop. For all other input combinations, the flip-flop reacts the same as those previously discussed. This type of flip-flop must be used as an output circuit for the core shift register because there is only a single data lead available from the register's output circuit (Fig. 8–15). This single lead is applied to the output flip-flop's set input; hence a 1 from the data line would "set" the flip-flop, but a 0 following the 1 could not "reset" the flip-flop since it also is wired to the set input. Therefore, the reset input of the override flip-flop has a constant minus voltage (1) applied that "resets" the flip-flop every time a 0 appears on the data output line going to the set input.

The modules used in the internal portion of the shift register use two cores, two transistors, and two resistors per bit of storage. The modules are connected in series, and the number used depends upon the number of bits of storage required. There will be two modules less than the total bits of storage needed because, as shown in Fig. 8–16, the input and output circuitry each store 1/2 bit, and the output flip-flop stores another bit. The schematic of two modules and their interconnections is shown in Fig. 8–18.

The following detailed discussion of the core shift register starts with the driver circuit and proceeds to the input circuitry, through the core modules, and then to the output circuitry. Figure 8–19 shows the schematic of the input, output, and driver circuits. In this particular example, the register contains 28 bits; therefore, there are 26 core modules. Also −3 V is true and 0 V (ground) is false. A further assumption must be that:

(a) When electron current is applied to the *non-dot* end of a winding, it sets the core to a *zero state*, and

(b) When electron current is applied to the *dot end* of a winding, it sets the core to the *one state*.

The *driver circuit* is like a two-way blocking oscillator utilizing two transistors in a closed-loop configuration. Since the driver is a symmetrical circuit, only one side need be described in detail. The driver input gate (Fig. 8-19) is held in the true state by logical gating when the register is "in use," and the junction of CR14 and CR13 would be at a true level voltage except that CR13 is forward-biased and holds this point at approximately ground potential. However, when the clock-pulse occurs, CR13 is reverse-biased and disconnects. The turn-on current for Q5 is now supplied by R20 through diodes CR11, CR12, and CR14. (Q5 is normally held cut-off by the positive potential taken from the voltage divider R18 and R17.)

During the clock time, the collector Q5 swings from −12 V to approximately ground. Q6 which was reverse-biased before clock time, is now forward-biased, and its base current is supplied by the collector of Q5. Since the base of Q6 is now at approximately ground potential and

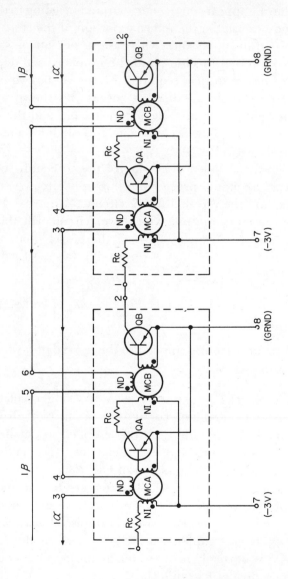

Fig. 8–18. Internal core modules.

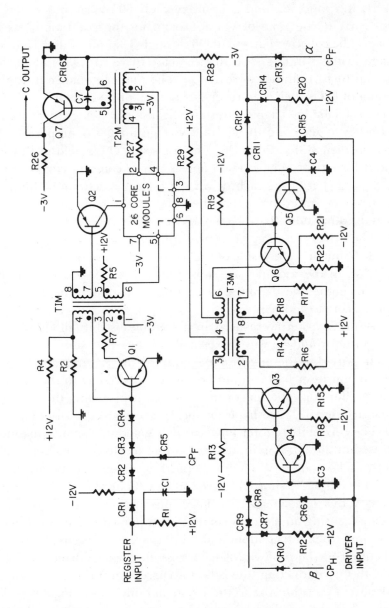

Fig. 8-19. Core register input-output shift control.

its VBE is approximately +0.8 V, the emitter is sitting at approximately −1 V. The emitter current is then controlled by the resistive combination of R21, R22, and R7, and is approximately 80 milliamperes. The collector-current rise time of Q6 approximates the rise time of its base voltage. The collector current of Q6 through T3M pins 7 and 8 induces a voltage in this winding such that the base drive for Q5 is maintained, which in turn continues to drive Q6. The induced voltage in the base winding of Q4 is such as to reverse-bias it to approximately +1 V. When the core of T3M has changed its state, the induced voltage in all windings diminishes to zero and the shut-off voltage for Q5 is supplied by R17, which in turn shuts down Q6. The transistor Q6 is held in the active region during the time it is on and is a true constant-current driver. The natural period of each driver is 1.5 msec. maximum, although if one driver is turned on before the other goes off, the one coming on forces the other one off.

The driver action is the same during the β period except the half-time clock initiates the β side of the driver. All of the cores, T1M, T2M, and T3M, in the modules are linked by either the α driver or the β driver, or both. These are the current pulses that shift the information from one core to another.

If the register were used in a continuous-shift mode only, the driver input would be wired externally to the −3 V supply. When the register is used in the on-off mode, both the driver input and the override flip-flop reset input would be connected directly to the output of the same flip-flop, booster, or inverter that is providing the logical on-off control signal. Waveshapes of these signals are shown in Fig. 8–17.

⑦ The core shift register *input circuit* is gated in a similar manner to that used in the flip-flop inputs. Zero input to the register has no effect on Q1, and when −3 V (true) is applied, it appears at the junction of CR2 and CR3 but is shorted to ground by CR5 until the full clock-pulse occurs. At this time, a negative voltage appears at the base of Q1, turning it on and causing an electron current from point 1 to 2 in T1M. Except at the time when a true input and a full clock-pulse occur, Q1 is always held cut-off by the positive voltage across the divider formed by R2 and R4. With Q1 conducting, the collector current in the 1 to 2 winding of T1M starts to set the core to the 1 state and induces a negative voltage at point 3 in the winding connected to the base. This induced voltage keeps the transistor on while the core is switching from the 0 state to the 1 state. When the core is completely set to the 1 state, the change in flux ceases, the base drive ceases, and the transistor turns off. The setting of the core, T1M, to the 1 state occurs during α time, when the input gate is true at the full-time clock-pulse.

(8) During β time, the β drive current applied to T1M (pins 5 and 6) causes the core to change state from the 1 state to the 0 state (both the I_α and the I_β current pulses build up with electron current into their +12-V supply). During the time the core is switching from the 1 state to the 0 state, a voltage is induced in the base winding (pins 7 and 8) which is connected to Q2. This induced voltage is a negative voltage of approximately 0.5 V amplitude, which is sufficient to turn on Q2 and cause a collector current. If the core T1M had, for some reason, been storing a 0, then no output at β time would occur at the collector of Q2 because the I would be attempting to set a core to 0 that was already 0 and no coupling flux would build up to create the necessary voltage out of windings 7 and 8.

In the *core modules* (Fig. 8–18), assume MC_A is in the 1 state. At α time, the shift current is applied to winding N_D of MC_A. The electron current enters pin 4 and the induced voltage in the windings of MC_A is positive at the dot ends of wiring with respect to the non-dot ends. The base-emitter junction of Q_A is forward-biased and its collector draws current. The collector swings up to ground, and the current, which is limited by the resistor R_C, passing through winding N_I of MC_B sets this core to the 1 state. The electron current into the dot end of N_I of MC_B causes the non-dot end of each winding to become positive with respect to the dot end. The induced voltage at the base of Q_B simply reverse-biases the transistor, and it remains off. During β time the β drive current is applied to N_D of MC_B. The induced voltage in N_D of MC_B holds the transistor on while the core is being read out. The collector of Q_B is connected to pin 1 on the next module and sets MC_A of that module to the 1 state. Now consider the other case, and assume MC_A is initially in the 0 state. At α time, the α drive current causes the state of the core to change from a 0 condition remanent flux to an active 0 quantity of flux, which is very little flux change (I_α is attempting to set a core to 0 that is already 0). Any voltage induced in the base winding will be very small, of short duration, and below the turn-on threshold of the transistor Q_A.

In the register *output circuitry*, the transistor Q7 (Fig. 8–19) is normally held on by the forward-bias current applied to the base through R28 and the base winding of T2M. With the transistor in saturation, its collector voltage is nearly ground potential. This output is connected directly to the set input of the magnetic core shift register override flip-flop. Assume S26 is storing a 1. At β time the 1 is read out

and the current pulse into pin 3 of T2M sets this core to the 1 state. At
α time, α drive current through the windings 1 and 2 of T2M resets
the core to the 0 state and the voltage induced in the base winding (pins
5 and 6) is positive at the dot end, which turns off Q7 for approximately
0.3 μsec. During this time, the collector current becomes 0 and the collector potential swings negative from approximately ground to -3 V.
This negative pulse occurs at approximately *0.1 μsec.* after the *full-time
clock-pulse.*

The set input of the override flip-flop is connected directly to the
C output of the register, and there is no clock-pulse applied to this
input. The reset input of the flip-flop is held in the true state by logical
gating and is a clocked input. At each full-time clock the flip-flop is
reset false. When a true output occurs at the C output of the register,
this pulse overrides the reset action and sets the flip-flop to the 1 state.
When a 0 is stored at T2M, no positive voltage is induced in the base
winding of Q7 at α time and the collector of Q7 remains at ground. The
logic and full-time clock applied to the reset input of the flip-flop resets
it to the 0 state.

8–12 Recirculating Register

When magnetic memories employing a moving surface (tapes,
drums) are used as the main storage device, it is common practice to
employ another form of register known as the *recirculating register*. If
the output from the last stage (LSD) of either a core or FF register is fed
back to the first stage, the data will continue to recirculate at the clock-
pulse rate until something interrupts them. This same effect can be
realized from a drum or tape by feeding the output of the read head
back to the write head in the same channel. The data are permanently
stored, but they are always moving because recirculation is accomplished
from a moving surface. When recirculating drum registers are used in a
given system, most of the system's main storage will be implemented
this way. This yields two main advantages:

(a) If a system happens to use a 30-bit word it would take 30 flip-flops
    to mechanize a register (normal or recirculating), but if a drum
    surface is used for recirculation only the read/write circuits (and
    possibly one "recirculation" FF) are needed.
(b) The access time to data stored on the drum is shortened.

If a recirculating register that "recirculates" just one word is desired, this is accomplished by inserting the word "data" onto the drum surface (or tape) at a write head, and then placing a read head down the channel a distance sufficient to store just this one word. The output of this read head is fed back to the original write head. (See Fig. 8–20.)

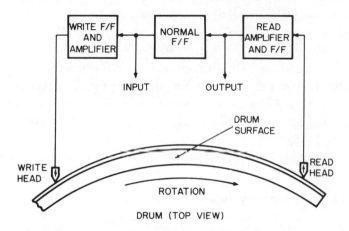

MILITARY SPECIFICATION SYMBOLS USED FOR READ AND WRITE HEADS

Fig. 8–20. Recirculating drum register.

If a 1 is written at the write head, it will be carried down the drum surface by the drum's rotation and after a determinable time will be read off by the read head and in turn passed to the recirculation flip-flop. It will be delayed in passing this flip-flop by one bit time (or, in essence, stored here for one bit time) and then it will pass on to the write flip-flop, will be rewritten on the drum, and will repeat the whole process. All the bits of one word can be written onto the drum surface (minus the one in the normal flip-flop) if the distance between heads is great enough. The distance between heads is a function of:

(a) The number of bits to be recirculated.
(b) The writing frequency (clock rate).
(c) The drum speed.

Often the actual physical size of the heads is a limiting factor. Using 50 to the inch (low loading density) it would take less than 1/2 inch of drum surface to recirculate a 25-bit word. The head construction (core, windings, and case) could make this small spacing a physical impossibility. However, if a one-word recirculating register is necessary, these factors would be considered in the original design. Generally, more than one word is recirculated — usually those pertaining to a given subject. The important considerations concerning the recirculating register are that the drum surface serves to replace a bank of flip-flops; the information can be recirculated indefinitely; it is available in a much shorter access time (that is, the written data do not have to traverse the whole drum before being read); and new data can be inserted at the input whenever a word requires changing. Notice carefully that any bits written on the drum to be recirculated are not destroyed when they pass the read head and will, of course, show up when the drum comes around, but they are destroyed when the write process takes place over them, just as an audio tape is erased by recording new "sounds" over the old. For that matter, there can be more than one recirculating register on a single drum channel and yet, because of the write/erase process, no register takes unwanted data from a previous register.

8-13 Other Memory Types

The preceding examples typify the most common memory devices in wide use at the time of this writing. There have been, and are, many unusual forms of memory that fall into the temporary, or register, class of memory. These include delay lines, high-persistence cathode-ray tubes, and character-holding cathode-ray tubes.

Of particular interest is the increasing use of the *disk memory* as a main memory device. This is essentially a drum memory insofar as the read/write techniques are concerned, but physically it is quite different. Several magnetic disks are evenly spaced along a common shaft (much like a stack of records) and the read/write heads may be along both the top and the bottom of each disk (Fig. 8-21). This creates lines of varying length under each head. Where recirculating registers are used on a normal drum, the recirculating lines are usually of different lengths anyway, so this is no disadvantage when using a disk. The inside lines on the disks would hold data that only needed short length for storage.

The main advantage of the disk memory is that it provides a very large amount of storage for a small quantity of space. Many large GP computers store their general, or voluminous, data on slow-speed, external tapes (not part of the fast main memory). The disk memory may replace much of this form of memory by being used in a "random" configuration. Under these circumstances, one read/write head bank is provided on a moving spindle allowing it to move up and down in front of the disk stack and also move in between to reach the desired channel.

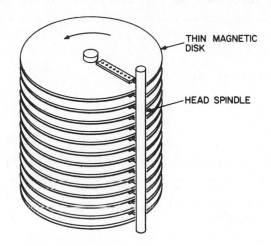

Fig. 8–21. Typical disk memory layout.

8–14 Conclusion

1. A large portion of digital computer mechanization comprises some sort of memory device, of which there are two classes:
   (a) Volatile.
   (b) Permanent.

2. The most common permanent memories are magnetic in nature and take the form of tapes, cores, and drums.
   (a) The tape is:
      Inexpensive and reliable and provides large storage capacity, but is fragile and slow.
   (b) The core is:
      Rugged and static and has very fast access, but is fairly expensive, comparatively difficult to read and requires extensive external circuitry.
   (c) The drum is:
      Easy to read, moderately fast, and provides large storage capacity, but is fairly expensive and requires rotational driving force.

3. Moving magnetic storage devices are best written on, or are read from, by pulses that change state in the middle of a bit time.

4. The term *register,* for most computers, refers to temporary storage arrays of flip-flops or cores that perform some function with a single "word." Registers may be loaded/read-out in parallel or serially.

Where the main memory employs a moving storage device, the term *recirculating register* refers to the elements between a write and read head, which are:

> write flip-flop and amplifier
> write head
> magnetic surface
> read head
> read amplifier and flip-flop
> recirculating flip-flop (may be incorporated in read FF)

5. Magnetic storage devices record both states. That is, the drum, tape, or core is not left demagnetized to represent a 0 and magnetized to represent a 1. Both directions of magnetization are used to represent the two states because an unmagnetized surface represents "no information"; therefore, if an unmagnetized area were to represent 0, 0 could not be distinguished from "no information." A 0 is one of the states and definitely represents data.

EXERCISES

1. What is the average length of time a good permanent storage device can retain data?

2. Why are materials that display a rectangular hysteresis curve preferred in magnetic computer memory devices?

3. What complications are involved in reading data from a core memory device?

4. Generally a drum memory is best suited for *(series)(parallel)* operation.

5. Since logic recorded on a drum by the Ferranti technique is peaked at half-clock pulse, how can the read circuits extract data at the full-time clock time?

6. The register is normally considered a temporary storage device and may be constructed of
    (a) part of a drum line
    (b) cores
    (c) flip-flops
    (d) any of these

7. What determines the minimum number of bits that may be stored on a drum recirculating register?

8. By using a half-clock pulse in the typical core shift register it is possible to
   (a) store twice as many bits as cores in the register.
   (b) Store the same number of bits as cores in the register.
   (c) Store information in half the time compared to conventional registers
   (d) None of these.

9. If clock pulses occur every 10 μsec., how long will it take to serially enter a 30-bit word into a register? To enter a 30-bit word in parallel into a register?

10. With a bit time of 5 μsec., what is the access time for a drum rotating at 33 rps?

11. How many bits are in the following word?

    011011110010

12. Describe what the word "format" means.

13. What is the function of an address?

14. Explain the meaning of access time.

15. If a drum stores 50 30-bit words on a channel and the clock pulses every 10 μsec., what is the access time?

16. Name two examples of volatile memories.

17. A core memory has 30 cores in the X plane and 60 cores in the Y plane. The device stores 37,800 bits. How long is a word for this memory?

18. Why doesn't $I/2$ destroy the state of the core?

19. When reading from core memories how is the state of the core detected?

20. Once data has been read from a core memory, and if the data is to be retained, what must be done?

21. If a computer core memory used 30-bit words, how many planes will the memory typically have?

9

ARITHMETIC UNIT

9–1 Introduction

Digital computers can be mechanized to perform all known arithmetic operations. The number of different arithmetic operations a given computer will perform depends on its expected usage. Almost all arithmetic operations can be reduced to some form of addition, subtraction, multiplication, or division. An examination of computer circuits that can perform these basic operations yields the fundamental knowledge needed· to mechanize more complicated mathematical circuits where desired.

Arithmetic circuits, like any computer circuit, can be mechanized to operate either in parallel or in series. We shall investigate each type of operation. Parallel operation, which examines each bit of a number simultaneously, is, of course, very rapid, but uses more equipment than the slower serial operation, which examines each bit consecutively.

9–2 Adders

The binary addition of all the possible combinations of two digits is considered in the accompanying truth table. Only the 1 + 1 situation

produces a carry. A simple two-input OR gate could take these combinations as inputs and produce the correct sum as an output except
when the $1 + 1$ combination occurs (Fig. 9-1).

Augend Digit	0	1	0	1
Addend Digit	0	0	1	1
Sum Digit	0	1	1	0
Carry Digit	0	0	0	1

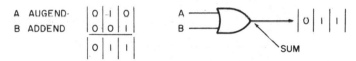

A   AUGEND·
B   ADDEND

Fig. 9-1. The OR gate used as an adder.

A. HALF-ADDER

A circuit device that will accept two inputs representing the augend
and addend digits and produce output signals representing the sum
and carry (in accordance with the truth table) is known as a *half-adder*.
The reason that the term *half* is employed is that this adder circuit can
only add together two variables at a time and does not consider the
possible carry signal that might have occurred from the next lower
order.

There are several ways of implementing the half-adder; two of the
more common techniques are shown in Fig. 9-2. These circuits may be
checked by performing the additions indicated in the truth table and
noting that the correct sum and carry is produced. (A typical characteristic of a half-adder is that it has two inputs and two outputs.) Figure
9-2B follows the logical development for binary addition, which is the
same as the exclusive OR gate development (Chapter 5): a true output
shall be produced when either of two inputs is true, but not when both
are false or both are true. In other words, the exclusive OR gate performs binary addition but does not produce a carry. The AND gate at
the bottom of Fig. 9-2B develops the carry.

Regardless of the circuit configuration used to accomplish half-adding, the logic remains the same; that is, there is logic defining the "sum" line and logic defining the "carry" line. This logic is developed

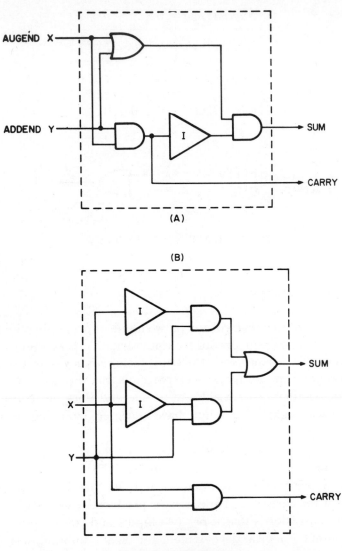

Fig. 9–2. Half-adders

from the truth table. For the sum logic, whenever a 1 appears in the "sum digit" line, an AND term is written; for the carry logic, whenever a 1 appears in the "carry" line an AND term is written. If the augend is represented by X and the addend by Y, the sum logic would be:

$$\text{sum} = XY' + X'Y \qquad \text{(exclusive OR condition)}$$

and the carry logic would be:

$$\text{carry} = XY$$

Notice that the half-adder of Fig. 9–2B is implemented directly from logic.

The correct addition of two numbers may be carried out by half-adders if several are connected together. For instance, the parallel addition of two third-order binary numbers is accomplished in Fig. 9–3. "$\Sigma/2$" in the figure signifies a half-adder.

$$\text{Augend:} \quad X_3 = 1, \quad X_2 = 1, \quad X_1 = 1$$
$$\text{Addend:} \quad Y_3 = 1, \quad Y_2 = 0, \quad Y_1 = 1$$

Except for the lowest order, it takes two half-adders plus an OR gate for each order of the operators being added. Notice that each unit contained within the dotted lines had *three* inputs and two outputs.

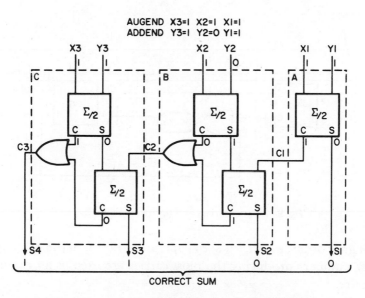

Fig. 9–3. Parallel binary addition using half-adders.

That is, these units, made up of half-adders, perform a full-adder function because they take into account the possibility of any carry from a previous order. In fact, each stage (except the LSB stage) does exactly what would have to be done on pencil and paper. Consider the example that follows.

Carry (from previous order) = 1

Augend (nth order)   = 1

Addend (nth order)   = 1

Examining each step performed and comparing it to the actual circuit (Fig. 9–3), we notice that first the augend and addend are added, the sum is "noted," and carry is pushed forward to next higher order (exactly as is done in the circuit); next, any previous carry is added to the "noted" sum, a new sum is generated, and any possible carry is pushed forward to the next higher order (again, exactly as done in the circuit).

Serial addition of two binary numbers may be accomplished in the manner shown in Fig. 9–4. The only additional circuit element needed is a delay (D, Fig. 9–4) of one bit time to move any possible carry into the

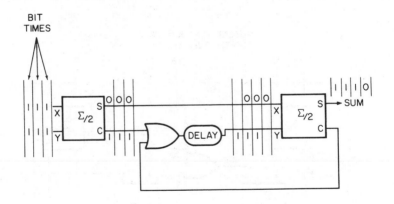

Fig. 9–4. Serial binary addition using half-adders.

next higher order, which, for serial operation, occurs at the next bit time. Binary numbers producing the most carries are used as an example in the figure.

B. FULL-ADDER

A full-adder circuit has *three* inputs and *two* outputs. The inputs are the addend, augend, and any possible carry from a preceding order. The outputs are a sum and any ensuing carry. Figure 9–5 shows a typical full-adder circuit. This full-adder may be checked by considering all the possible combinations of three inputs.

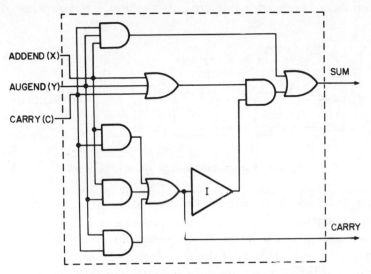

Fig. 9–5. Full-adder.

INPUTS			OUTPUTS	
X	Y	C	Sum	Carry
0	0	0	0	0
0	1	0	1	0
1	0	0	1	0
1	1	0	0	1
0	0	1	1	0
0	1	1	0	1
1	0	1	0	1
1	1	1	1	1

The process of using full-adders to form a parallel binary addition unit involves no extra circuitry and only one full-adder per order of the numbers being added. Figure 9–6 indicates the process of con-

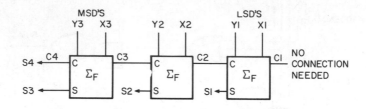

Fig. 9–6. Parallel binary adder using full-adders.

necting full-adders in parallel for the addition of two third-order binary numbers.

A full-adder can be used for serial binary addition by simply incorporating a single one-bit delay network to move the carry forward to the next order which occurs at the next bit time. (See Fig. 9–7.)

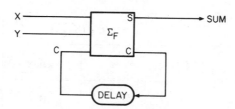

Fig. 9–7. Serial binary adder using full-adders.

9–3 Subtracters

A subtracter circuit by itself is probably of more academic than practical value since most computers subtract by the complementing and adding method utilizing adder circuits already mechanized. However, we shall examine first a possible half-subtracter circuit, and then the more practical technique of subtraction by complementing, using full-adders.

The combination of two variables by the rules of subtraction indicates that a borrow function is produced, or is necessary, when 1 is subtracted from 0, but the difference line (D) is exactly the same as a sum line for two variables and is, in fact, an exclusive OR configuration.

The half-subtracter, like the half-adder, has two input units and two output units, but the minuend and subtrahend inputs are not inter-changeable as are the augend and addend inputs of the adder. Also, the

Minuend	(M)	0	1	0	1
Subtrahend	(S)	0	0	1	1
Difference	(D)	0	1	1	0
Borrow	(B)	0	0	1	0

half-subtracter outputs will be a "difference" line and a "borrow" line, and not a "sum" line and a "carry" line. The logic equations for the subtraction truth table are:

$$\text{difference } (D) = MS' + M'S \text{ (exclusive OR term)}$$

$$\text{borrow } (B) = M'S$$

This can be implemented as shown in Fig. 9–8.

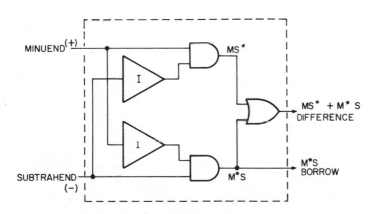

Fig. 9–8. Half-subtractor logic diagram.

As with half-adder circuits, the half-subtracter can be connected in a proper parallel or series configuration and produce a *correct* differ-ence. Figures 9–9 and 9–10 show typical binary subtracter mechaniza-tions using half-subtracters. The application of any binary values where $M > S$ will prove these circuits. Notice the similarity between these circuits and the comparable adder circuits (the delay is one bit time). The outstanding difference is that the connections *must* be made as shown. The "borrow" out of the first stage must go to the subtrahend

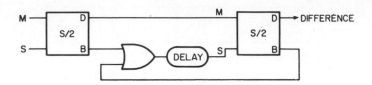

Fig. 9–9. Serial subtraction using half-subtracters.

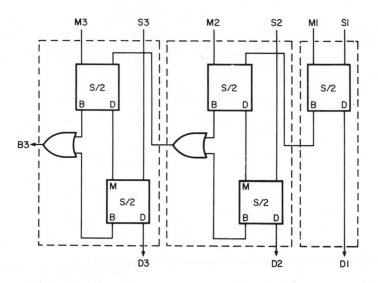

Fig. 9–10. Parallel subtraction using half-subtracters.

lead (not the minuend lead) of the second stage. Subtracters using full-subtracter elements can also be mechanized, but they add little to our understanding of typical arithmetic units since they are very much like the full-adder circuits already considered.

9–4 Combination Circuits

It is more common, in an actual computer, to perform subtraction by complementing and adding since the adder circuits have already been mechanized and may be used for subtraction as well as addition. The process of performing subtraction by this method is simply to complement (invert) the subtrahend before it enters either of the input leads (augend or addend) of the adder circuit. For instance, the parallel full-adder unit shown in Fig. 9–5 (for three-digit numbers) may double as a binary subtracter when implemented as shown in Fig. 9–11. When

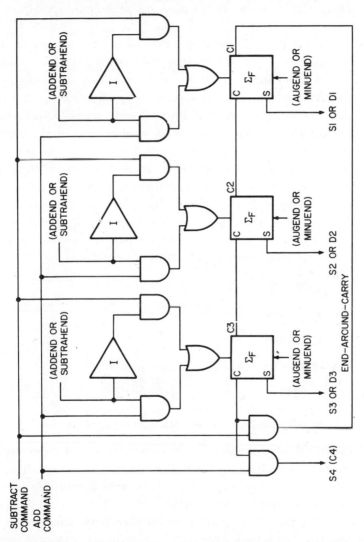

Fig. 9–11. Combination parallel adder and subtracter.

a program step indicates a "subtract order," the "subtract command" (or "subtract instruction") line will go "hot" ("true" logic voltage). (See Sec. 7–16, describing program.) When this line goes hot, the AND gate after the inverter is opened and the subtrahend enters the full-adder complemented (one's complement). At this time the end-around-carry gate is also opened, inserting C4 back into C1. When an "add command" occurs, the binary adder operates normally. The process of complementing and "adding back" the end-around-carry produces the correct difference on S1, S2, and S3. In a similar manner, parallel binary subtraction may be performed on adders composed of half-adders.

When subtraction is being performed on a serial arithmetic circuit, complementing one of the inputs (Fig. 9–7) yields a difference answer, but unless a 1 from some external source is added to the LSD of the answer, the answer is in error by some very small amount. That is, the LSD will have been produced and have already moved down the line before the superfluous MSD (used as the end-around-carry) is present to be added back on the LSD. Very often the error in the LSD can be ignored, especially where the operators are words containing approximately 10 bits or more. The unneeded MSD will be lost when the answer is stored in a register, since it would require a place one greater than the number of bits in the original operators. For instance, if the word length of a given computer were 10 bits, then the subtraction, by complementing, of the following values would appear as:

$$
\begin{array}{ll}
0001011001 & \\
& \text{registers completely full} \\
\underline{0000011011} & \\
\\
0001011001 & \\
+\ 1111100100 & \text{one's complement} \\
\textcircled{1}0000111101 & \text{answer (in error by 01)} \\
\end{array}
$$

⌐MSD lost, will not fit into 10-bit storage register

The preceding examples for binary adders and subtracters indicate only the basis for many special arithmetic circuits, such as those necessary to perform algebraic addition and subtraction. These special circuits are too numerous to cover in this text.

It is well to note that an adder/subtracter arithmetic circuit, in its entirety, usually encompasses the necessary temporary storage registers to hold the individual operators and any answer. For instance, Fig. 9–12 shows all the flip-flop registers that might be used to hold operators and the answer for a parallel adder involving four-bit words.

Often the addend register serves as both addend and answer store.

Once the addend data have moved into the adders, this register is un-used and can receive the sum. When this register serves double duty it is often called the *accumulator register*.

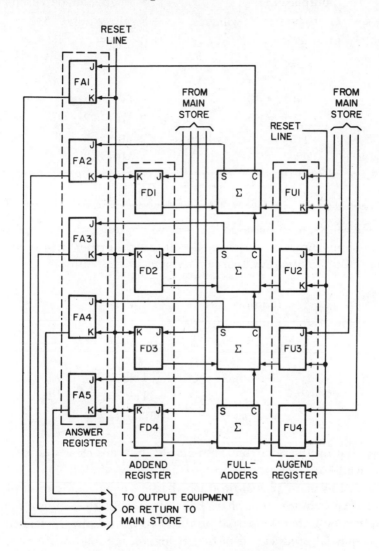

Fig. 9-12. Arithmetic circuit with registers.

9-5 Multipliers

Most multiplication (and division) is carried out on the existing adders in a computer with some additional control circuitry. This is possible since multiplication is, in reality, simply repeated addition. That is:

$$
\begin{array}{rl}
8 & \text{multiplicand} \\
\times 3 & \text{multiplier} \\
\hline
24 & \text{product}
\end{array}
\qquad \text{which is:} \qquad
\begin{array}{rl}
8 & \text{eight added to itself} \\
+8 & \text{three times} \\
+8 & \\
\hline
24 &
\end{array}
$$

or

$$
\begin{array}{rl}
1101 & = 13 \\
\times 101 & = 5 \\
\hline
1101 & \\
0000 & \\
1101 & \\
\hline
1000001 & = 65
\end{array}
\qquad \text{which is:} \qquad
\begin{array}{ll}
1101 & (1) \\
+1101 & (2) \\
+1101 & (3) \\
+1101 & (4) \\
+1101 & (5) \\
\hline
1000001 &
\end{array}
$$

In other words, multiplication is a process of adding the multiplicant to *itself* as many times as the *multiplier* dictates. Further investigation of binary multiplication reveals other characteristics. For instance:

$$
\begin{array}{lll}
\text{multiplicand} & & 1111 \\
\text{multiplier} & & \times 1101 \\
\hline
& A & 1111 \\
\text{partial} & B & 0000 \\
\text{products} & C & 1111 \\
& D & 1111 \\
\hline
\text{product} & & 11000011
\end{array}
$$

The partial products for binary multiplication are clearly equal to the multiplicand or equal to zero and, in fact, the product is obtained by the addition of as many partial products that are equal to the multiplicand as there are 1s in the multiplier. The only catch to this straight forward multiplication is that the partial products do not occupy the same order. That is, partial product C is of higher magnitude than A; the reason is, of course, that C was "developed" by the second most significant 1 in the multiplier. A correct product may be obtained for any binary multiplication if the multiplicand is added to itself as many times as there are 1s in the multiplier and these additions take place in the right order. A method of determining the proper order would significantly save time over the method of simply adding the multiplicant to itself as many times as the multiplier indicates. For example, the preceding problem is:

$$
\begin{array}{rcr}
1111 & = & 15 \\
\underline{1101} & = & \underline{\times 13} \\
11000011 & = & 195
\end{array}
$$

This indicates that had the "repeated addition" method been used, the multiplicand would have had to be added to itself 13 times, whereas, had the proper order of partial products been determined, the multiplicand would need to be added to itself (in proper order) only three times. Relatively speaking, the partial product C is to the left of the partial products B and A, and D is to the left of C, B, and A. Or, A is to the right of B; B is to the right of C; etc. Suppose the given example is handled as shown in Fig. 9–13.

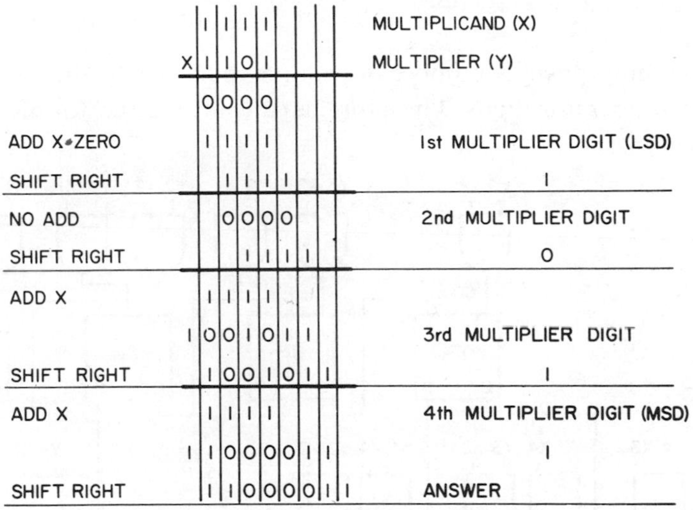

Fig. 9–13. Sample shift multiplication.

RULE: When 1 occurs in the multiplier, add the multiplicand to the last partial product and shift right.

When 0 occurs in the multiplier do not add, just shift right.

The preceding examples indicate that to use the already existing binary adders to perform binary multiplication we need a new circuit control: either a device to tell the adder *how many* times to add the multiplicand to itself (how many depending on the value of the multiplier), or a device to perform the proper shifting.

Where speed is essential, it is possible to perform multiplication in one step. Figure 9–14 shows a "simultaneous" multiplier good for multiplying only four digits times four digits in approximately one bit time. It is apparent from this figure why most computers use existing adder circuits, since most computers will be operating on more than four digits. Notice also the number of possible digits in a multiplication answer. If four-digit operators are used, the maximum number of digits in the answer would be:

$$
\begin{array}{r}
1111 \\
\times\, 1111 \\
\hline
1111 \\
1111 \\
1111 \\
1111 \\
\hline
11100001 \quad \text{eight-digit answer}
\end{array}
$$

The maximum possible number of product digits will be the sum of the number of operator digits. Therefore, an answer register for multiplica-

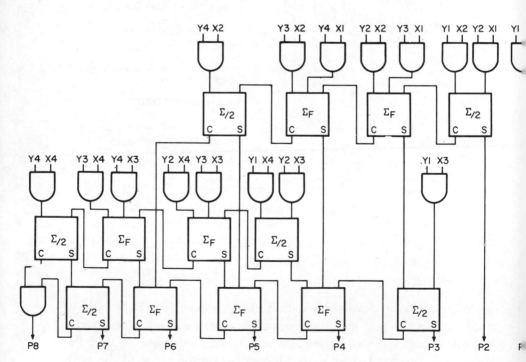

Fig. 9–14. Simultaneous multiplier.

tion products would have to be large enough to hold any possible product.

As with adders and subtracters there are several possible circuit configurations to perform multiplication by repeated addition or by the shifting technique. Multiplication by repeated addition requires a circuit component not yet discussed: the counter. Figure 9–15 shows the basic technique employed for repeated-addition multiplication. The value of the multiplicand is loaded into the multiplicand register and the value of the multiplier is loaded into the multiplier counter. The multiplier counter will usually be mechanized to start with an inserted

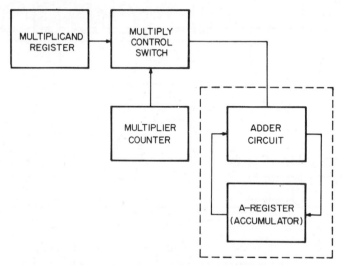

Fig. 9–15. Repeated addition multiplier.

count (the value of the multiplier) and count down to zero. That is, should binary 101 (5) be inserted, the counter would register 100 (4) at the next bit time, 011 (3) at the next bit time, and so on to zero. At count zero, the multiply control switch would be closed, halting the repeated addition process. As long as the multiply control switch is open, the value in the multiplicand register will be added, each bit time, to the existing value in the A-register. The multiplicand and A-register outputs comprise the augend and addend inputs to the adder circuit. The A-register always holds the answer from the last addition. The A-register starts out, of course, with zero, and as the repeated additions continue, the value in the A-register grows. If the A-register is to hold an accurate answer, it will need to have as many flip-flops as

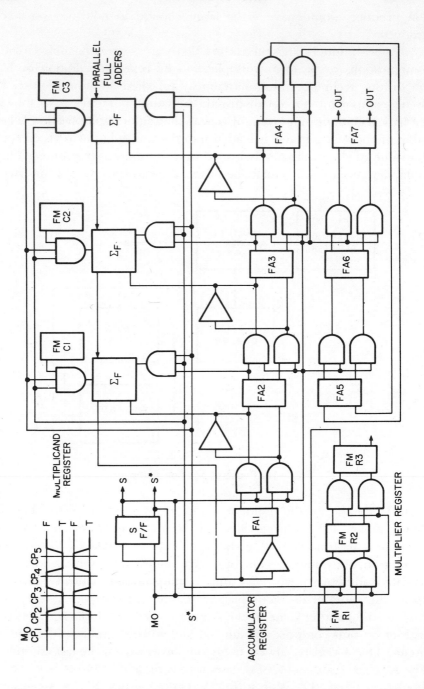

Fig. 9–16. Shifting multiplier.

the sum of the digits in both operators. That portion of the multiplier circuit that contains the adder and A-register (dotted lines) is loosely known as an *accumulator* (hence, the term A-register). The A-register is actually "accumulating" each partial sum and eventually holds the final answer.

Repeated-addition multiplying is the most time-consuming technique for developing products, but it is a simple technique and requires only one extra piece of equipment (the counter). Actually, this method is time-consuming only in respect to the given computer. As far as the "outside world" is concerned, this method produces product answers as fast as they could ever be used by a human operator (usually it takes about 150 to 1000 μsec. for an average multiplication operation). However, the rest of the computer circuits may need to use the arithmetic circuits, and they may find this time too long.

The basic technique for multiplication by the "shifting method" requires some additional control pulses (other than clock-pulses) that generally will be developed in the control and timing unit of a computer, but they can be, for this discussion, developed at the multiplier circuit. The rule for multiplying by shifting indicates that for each step of the operation a "shift" occurs, whether an add takes place or not (Fig. 9–13). This means that each step takes at least two bit times: one for adding or not adding, and one for shifting. Figure 9–16 shows an exemplary circuit used to accomplish "shift multiplying." The shift control flip-flop alternately "sets" and "resets" itself, thereby providing a "true" signal (S) every other bit time. The output of this flip-flop controls the action of "add or not add" during one bit time (S*), "shift" during the next bit time (S).

The most convenient way to understand this circuit is to trace through the multiplication of two numbers, say, 101×111. The multiplicand and multiplier registers are first reset, then loaded with the operators. Loading can be accomplished in parallel or in series. Connections are not shown; therefore, assume loading has taken place. The multiplication process will be started by a command pulse (M_0) from the programming unit. This pulse resets the shift control flip-flop, which puts the S output at "false" level and the S* output at "true" level; hence, the first action that can occur (in conjunction with the first clock-pulse) is an "add" or "not add" depending on the state of multiplier flip-flop FMR3. The sequence of operation is as follows (for 101×111):

A. M_0 resets S flip-flop.

B. The output of FMR3 is true level; S* is true level; therefore, the parallel adders add the contents of FMC1–FMC3 and FA2–FA4 and·deposit the sum back in FA1–FA4.

C. Since the accumulator register was initially all zero, the sum is equal to the multiplicand. (111), and this value is the sum answer in FA2–FA4.

D. At the next clock-pulse, S output is "true," and S* output is "false"; hence, no more adding can take place, but a shift-right occurs in both the multiplier and accumulator registers.

E. At the next clock-pulse, S* is "true," S is "false," and the adders would try to add the contents of FMC1–FMC3 to the contents of FA2–FA4, but the control action of FMR3 (which is now "false") does not allow this addition to take·place.

F. At the next clock-pulse, a right-shift occurs and the accumulator register is now loaded:

$$FA1 = 0 \qquad FA5 = 1$$
$$FA2 = 0 \qquad FA6 = 1$$
$$FA3 = 0 \qquad FA7 = 0$$
$$FA4 = 1$$

G. At the next clock-pulse an add does take place because the MSD of the multiplier (101) has shifted into FMR3.

H. The addition that takes place is:

111	MC register
0001110	accumulator register
100011	final true product

I. Although the correct product now exists in the accumulator register, the shift will take place automatically, placing the product LSD into FA7. The accumulator is now ready to be unloaded, which could occur either serially or in parallel.

In a normal computer, a "stop multiplication" pulse from the control unit would at this time disengage the multiplier circuit.

The preceding example uses parallel addition and would, therefore, be classed as a parallel multiplier. The same techniques could be employed to implement a serial multiplier. This circuit does not indicate all the control pulses that would be available in an actual machine; it serves only to illustrate the technique of "shift" multiplying.

9-6 Dividers

As with multiplication, a separate circuit can be implemented to do only division. (See simultaneous multiplication, Fig. 9–14.) However, this type of circuit for binary numbers of any magnitude (approximately 10 bits) would involve a huge number of gates and subtracters. Such a circuit may be set up where speed is essential, but, since division, like multiplication, can make use of existing adder/subtracter circuits, most computers do not have straight dividing circuits.

Division is actually only repeated subtraction . That is:

$$
\begin{array}{r}
3 \\
\hline 8\,)\,24
\end{array}
\quad \text{or} \quad
\begin{array}{rl}
\text{dividend} & 24 \\
\text{divisor} & \underline{-8} \quad \text{subtraction 1} \\
& 16 \\
& \underline{-8} \quad \text{subtraction 2} \\
& 8 \\
& \underline{-8} \quad \text{subtraction 3} = \text{quotient} \\
\text{remainder} & 0
\end{array}
$$

Unlike the repeated-addition method of multiplication, where the value of the multiplier was loaded into a counter and counted down, the repeated-subtraction method of division loads *the number of subtractions* that take place into the counter. The counter, then holds the answer.

Basically, the repeated-subtraction technique of division is shown in Fig. 9–17. At the start of a division, the dividend would be loaded into

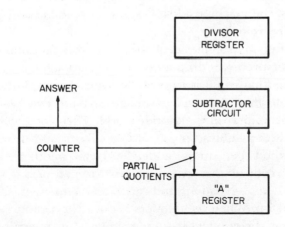

Fig. 9–17. Repeated subtraction divider.

the A-register and the divisor into the divisor register. As each sub-traction took place, the value in the A-register would become smaller and smaller, finally reaching zero (or some remainder), and the count in the counter would become larger and larger, finally yielding the correct quotient. The problem with a divider circuit is that it does not stop when the A-register reaches zero (or some remainder), whereas the repeated addition (for multiplication) stopped automatically when the counter reached zero. The subtracter will actually try to continue subtracting beyond the point of zero remainder, but when it does, the value in the A-register becomes a negative quantity. This negative quantity can be recognized in arithmetic circuits that handle values with different signs (algebraic manipulation) in a "sign comparator" unit; a negative stops the divide process and "adds-back" the overage. This is illustrated below:

Problem: 21 divided by $8 = 2\frac{5}{8}$, which is:

$$
\begin{array}{ll}
21 & \\
\underline{-8} & \text{subtraction 1} \\
+13 & \\
\underline{-8} & \text{subtraction 2 (quotient)} \\
+5 & \\
\underline{-8} & \text{subtraction 3 (overdraft)} \\
-3 & \text{negative remainder (sensed in sign comparator)} \\
\underline{+8} & \text{restore addition} \\
+5 & \text{Restored (true) remainder}
\end{array}
$$

The machine actually subtracts one step too far. When the negative value occurs, the machine adds-back the subtrahend and produces the correct positive remainder.

Very often in machines dealing with large binary numbers many of the arithmetic processes drop a few of the least significant digits in the answers. The final result is in error to some degree, but is usually far more accurate than the analog voltage that will eventually represent these binary numbers in the outside world. Therefore, when division is being done with a subtracter circuit that subtracts by the complement-and-add method (i.e., using "adder" circuits), another form of "stop subtraction" control that does not produce an actual remainder is available. When the end-around-carry ceases to occur, the repeated subtractions stop. When the quotient is even, the answer is 100 per cent accurate; when the quotient has a remainder, the answer is rounded off, as shown below.

Given: (A) 8 divided by $2=4$; (B) 8 divided by $3=2\frac{2}{3}$.

(A)   1000   (B)   1000
     $\div$ 10 $\div$ 11
         1000   1000
(1) $+1101$ (comp.)   (1) $+1100$ (comp.)
      ①0101   ①0100
      └─→ 1   └─→ 1
       0110   0101
(2) $+1101$ (2) $+1100$
      ①0011   ①0001
      └─→ 1   └─→ 1
       0100   0010
(3) $+1101$ Ans. (3) $+1100$
      ①0001   ⓪1110
      └─→ 1   └─→ 0
       0010   1110
Ans. (4) $+1101$
      ⓪1111   no carry — stop
      └─→ 0
       1111   Answer is 3 instead of $2\frac{2}{3}$.
                                    This inaccuracy would be
 no carry — stop   very slight for large binary
                                    numbers.

Other techniques are available besides those described above. Often a given computer has particular control signals available from the "control and timing" area to regulate both the multiplication and division processes.

Circuits similar to those used to perform multiplication by "shifting-right" are employed in division, the only difference being the direction of shift. The dividend can be loaded into an accumulator register and the divisor into a divisor register, and an additional register provided to hold the ensuing quotient (Fig. 9–18).

A shift-left always occurs in the accumulator and in the quotient register, and a zero or one is posted in the quotient register for each step of the division. A zero is posted when a subtraction cannot be performed, and a one when a subtraction can be performed. Notice, the divisor is fed into the subtracter circuit corresponding to the digits of highest order of the dividend.

EXAMPLE:

```
        100                5
1001)101101            9)45
        1001
        ─────
         1001
         1001
         ─────
         0000
```

```
         101101     accumulator register
  1     − 100100     divisor register
         ──────
         001001
         010010 ◄── shift left
  0     − 100100     won't subtract (post zero)
         ──────
         100100      shift left
         ──────
         100100
  1◄──  − 100100 ◄── subtracts OK (post one)
         ──────
         000000
```

Answer: $101 = 5$

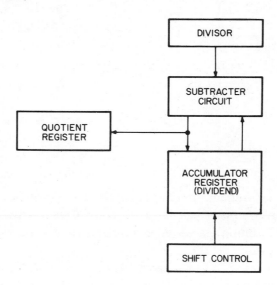

Fig. 9–18. Dividing by shifting circuit.

9–7 Conclusion

A. Adder circuits are classed as:

　　1. Half-adders:

　　　　a. augend and addend inputs (two inputs)

　　　　b. sum and carry outputs (two outputs).

2. Full-subtracters:
   a. augend, addend, and previous carry inputs (three inputs)
   b. sum and carry outputs (two outputs).

B. Full-adders can be mechanized from half-adders.

C. Subtracter circuits are classed as:
   1. Half-subtracters:
      a. minuend and subtrahend inputs (two inputs)
      b. difference and borrow outputs (two outputs).
   2. Full-adders:
      a. minuend subtrahend, and previous borrow inputs (three input)s
      b. difference and borrow outputs (two outputs).

D. Subtracter circuit leads must be connected properly: minuend to minuend, etc.

E. Subtracter circuits can be mechanized from adders by using the complement method and providing for end-around-carry.

F. Multiplication is usually performed by either:
   1. The repeated-addition technique, or
   2. The shift technique.

G. Division is usually performed by either:
   1. The repeated-subtraction technique, or
   2. The shift technique.

H. All arithmetic circuits may be mechanized in series or in parallel.

ARITHMETIC UNIT EXERCISES

1. What is the largest product that can occur when two three-bit binary numbers are multiplied?

2. Serial adding may be accomplished using (one)(two)(three)(four) half-adders.

3. The difference term from a half-subtracter circuit can be derived from the same exclusive OR gate circuit as the sum term for a half-adder except that the _____ gate must be replaced by a _____ gate to complete the half-subtractor circuit.

4. Draw a full-adder circuit using half-adders.

5. Write the logic for, and implement, a full-subtracter circuit.

6. How many inputs can a half-adder accept; can a full-adder accept? How many outputs does each of the adders have?

7. Explain how a subtraction can be performed by using a full-adder circuit.

8. Multiplication can be performed by the repeated addition method or by the SHIFT method. Can the repeated addition method ever require less time to perform than the SHIFT method? Explain.

9. What two methods are used in division?

10. The division process is complicated by the fact that the quotient may be _____.

11. Write the input equations to a half-adder that will produce the complemented output. (Use a truth table.)

12. Draw an adder circuit, using logic symbols, that will serially add two numbers yielding a correct sum on a single line.

10

INPUT-OUTPUT UNIT

10-1 Introduction

The input-output unit reconciles the "world" or the digital computer with the real world, which is different from that of the computer in at least two important ways:

(1) The real world is not digital, but analog.
(2) The real world operates on a relatively slow time-scale.

Although the input-output unit performs what could be considered an auxiliary function in the over-all computer organization (it does not do any actual "digital computing"), it is, in practically all commercial computers, the most extensive single unit. The input group must be able to encode (change information from any form *to* digital form), and the output group must decode (change *from* digital form to any usable form). The input-output unit must also make up as much as possible for the great time differences.

General-purpose computers stand waiting to solve problems presented to them by human operators. Special-purpose machines are directly connected, through their inputs, to a special problem and solve only this problem when it arises. Many computers are a combination

167

of both types. Computers used for tactical military situations generally serve both purposes. For instance, a tactical computer may be constantly tracking airborne targets without being commanded to do so (special purpose), while at any time a human operator may request the computer to plot a projectile path from a missile battery to target (general purpose).

Where human operators must "command" a computer, it is sometimes advantageous to give the commands to the computer in a form that is already digital. A straight manual keyboard is the simplest type of input-output device. The keyboard is a typewriter on which commands are typed out according to a code. In turn, the computer output circuits may automatically type out the answers on the same typewriter (Fig. 10-1A and B).

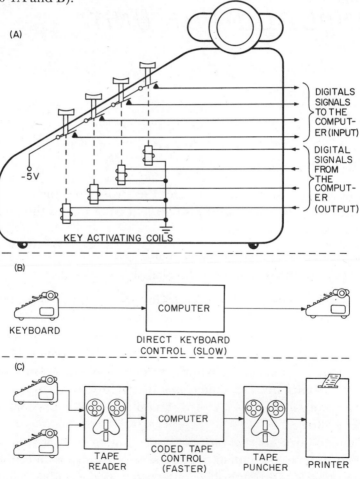

Fig. 10–1. Manual keyboard.

This form of input-output is obviously slow, since the computer must wait for the operator to type and the operator is further hindered by having to type according to a code. To speed up this method, the typewriter may be specially designed to place typed commands, in advance, on punched paper tape, or perhaps magnetic tape.

Now the computer does not have to wait for the operator to type out messages, since the computer can read directly from the punched tape. That is, large quantities of tapes can be made in advance by many operators handling different problems on different tape-punching typewriters, and the computer looks at these tapes from its "tape reader." As indicated in Fig. 10–1C, the computer will control a tape-punching device, and these tapes in turn can be used to run a printer or the same typewriters that made the input tapes.

There are currently many forms of coded inputs. The most popular are punched paper tapes, magnetic tapes, and punched cards. These tapes or cards will have been prepared well in advance of their date of use.

The next most critical point of delay is at the output end. Here, however, the *computer* is punching tapes or cards as solutions to problems are finished, and automatic typing devices are very fast. They are, of course, not as fast as the electronic circuitry within the computer, but they have a chance of keeping pace with the computer because many internal computer calculations require repeated steps.

In a further effort to "smooth" time differences, most computer input-output units contain a buffer storage element. This storage may be composed of temporary, flip-flop registers, a small drum or core matrix, or sometimes even part of the main memory element. For example, an output buffer may be composed of three registers, A, B, and C. Register A could be loaded with the answer to a finished problem at the normal speed of the computer. Now, register A could unload into a tape puncher at a slower rate than it was loaded. While register A is unloading, register B could be loading with another problem from the computer, etc. The coded tapes and buffer stores act together as "time reservoirs."

Large general-purpose computers are very expensive. Money is lost when they sit idle; hence they must be kept busy. A special-purpose computer is built for a special application; as long as it performs this function, it is economical. Where a special-purpose computer is tracking aircraft, its inputs are probably radar pulses, and although these pulses may not come as often as the computer could use them, as long as tracking is accomplished, the computer is well used. Outputs from the special-purpose computer are usually fed directly to electronic devices such as indicator scopes or readout lights and they, of course, can use computer outputs as fast as the computer can produce them. Input-output devices

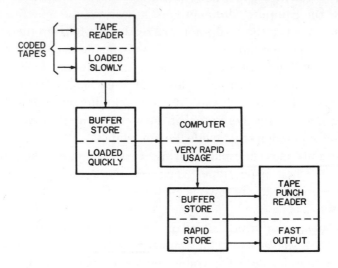

Fig. 10–2. Input-output data flow.

for special purpose computers do not present the problem of mechanical slowness (as do those for general purpose computers), but rather that of changing analog voltages (such as radar video) to digital signals.

10–2 Encoding-Decoding Techniques

A. ENCODING

Encoding involves changing inputs of any form to a digital form. The most common encoding involves changes of:

(a) digital-to-digital.
(b) analog-to-digital.

Digital-to-digital conversions are a problem of time and amplitude adjustment. The digital inputs may be operating on a slower or faster clock-rate than the internal computer. Very often the incoming clock-rate is slower. For instance, a digital word of 10 bits might be coming in to the computer from a data link line (digital radio communication line), where each bit is represented by a pulse lasting 10 msec., defined by a train of 1-msec-wide clock-pulses. If the incoming "word" of information is 1101001110 (10 bits), the data would appear as shown in Fig. 10–3A.

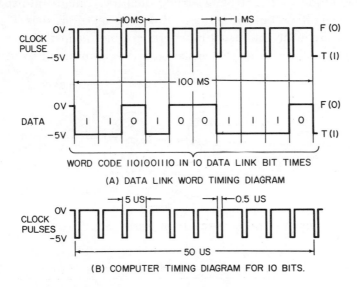

WORD CODE 1101001110 IN 10 DATA LINK BIT TIMES

(A) DATA LINK WORD TIMING DIAGRAM

(B) COMPUTER TIMING DIAGRAM FOR 10 BITS.

Fig. 10–3. Sample digital-to-digital encoding.

Now, the computer may be operating with a 5.0 μsec. bit time and a clock-pulse width of 0.5 μsec. The computer timing would appear as shown in Fig. 10–3B.

If the data link word is coming in serially, 100 μsec. must elapse before the 10-bit word is completely received. The computer could handle a serial 10-bit word in only 50 μsec Obviously, the input unit of the computer must sample each digit as it becomes available and store these digits, one at a time, until the entire 10-bit word is assembled. When the storage, or "buffer," register is full, it may be transferred out at the computer's rate.

Besides timing adjustments, digital-to-digital conversions may require adjustment of the logic levels (amplitude changes). For instance, it may be necessary to change the logic where incoming data are true at + 15 V to true at −5 V This, of course, is only a problem of inverting and clipping.

Analog-to-digital conversion (sometimes called "anadig" or, more popularly, "andacon") presents more problems than digital-to-digital.

Even the conversion of a scaled analog signal often loads the signal and affects its magnitude. A device that has met with wide success in the solution of this problem is the so-called *shaft digitizer* or *disk encoder*. A motor armature is caused to rotate through some angle depending on the magnitude of the driving analog quantity. Binary information is then picked off a set of commutated disks by a set of brushes (Fig. 10-4). For each angle of the armature there is some distinct binary output from the bank of brushes. For instance, if the commutator were laid out

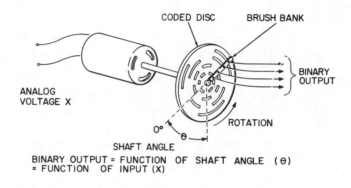

BINARY OUTPUT = FUNCTION OF SHAFT ANGLE (θ)
= FUNCTION OF INPUT (X)

(A) MOTOR AND DISK

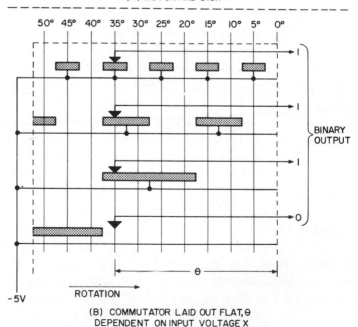

(B) COMMUTATOR LAID OUT FLAT, θ
DEPENDENT ON INPUT VOLTAGE X

Fig. 10–4. Sample disk encoder.

flat, as in Fig. 10–4B, four of the brushes (at an armature angle θ corresponding to an analog input voltage X) would "read" the indicated binary code. For every five degrees of rotation, the output digital code is different. This type of andacon conversion is also accomplished by using a commutator that is part of the rotating armature shaft. That is, the brushes are mounted along the motor shaft and there is no disk. This is called a *shaft encoder*. In either case, accuracy of encoding is determined by the number of brushes used and the degree of shaft rotation per volt of input.

Another type of analog conversion technique in popular use is the so-called *ladder* or *current weighter* circuit. This device handles the analog voltage directly; hence care must be taken that the conversion circuitry does not significantly alter the input analog signal (Fig. 10–5).

Precision currents produced in the input unit are compared with incoming signal currents. The basic principle of operation is that if the incoming signal is, for instance, +1.0 ma, and is compared with −1.0 ma, the output is some binary code; if the input is +0.5 ma, comparing this with −0.5 ma produces some other binary code output. The actual comparison takes place in steps. For instance, the analog input may be +1.5 ma of current. This input is first compared with an internal, precision current of −0.5 ma. There is a difference current of +1.0 ma, which sets the first bit of an output code true. The next comparison is the +1.5-ma input against a precision current of −1.0 ma. There is now a +0.5 ma difference, which sets the next bit of the output code true. The next comparison is: analog input of +1.5 ma against −1.5 ma precision = 0 ma difference, setting the next bit of output code false. Binary output for +1.5 ma analog input is 110.

The analog input is scaled down or up to a certain limit of current. This stage also serves to isolate the analog voltage from the converter. Switches S1–S4 are logically controlled by clock-pulses and the outputs of flip-flops F1–F4. Any difference of current is applied to the error amplifier A_E.

At clock-pulse time one (CP1), S1 automatically closes and a comparison of −1.0 ma precision current is made with the input current. If the input current is the greater, the error (difference) current causes the error amplifier to have a true output, which at CP1 passes through gate one and sets F1 high. F1's going high holds S1 closed. At CP2, S2 automatically closes and adds −0.5 ma of current to that passing through S1, giving +1.5 ma of precision current. If this second comparison yields another true output from the error amplifier, gate 2 is opened and F2 is set high. F2's being high holds S2 closed. At CP3, S3 automatically closes and adds −0.25 ma to the existing −1.5 ma, and the next comparison may find the precision current of +1.75 ma higher than the input

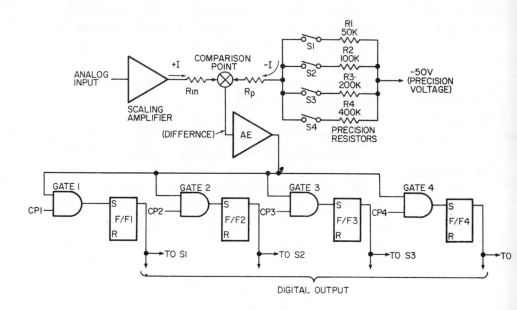

Fig. 10–5. Simplified ladder andacon.

current. If this is the case, the output of the error amplifier is false, gate 3 does not pass a signal, and F3 stays low (false). With F3 low, switch S3 does not hold closed, and the −0.25 ma of precision current drops out. At CP4, S4 automatically closes and adds −0.125 ma to the existing −1.5 ma and another comparison is made. Additional legs in the precision bank add in successively smaller increments of current at each clock time until the incoming current is very nearly matched. At the time all precision switches have been sequentially closed, a digital code exists at the output flip-flops representing the input current.

There are, of course, many other types of encoding circuits designed to suit particular situations. They are too numerous to mention here.

B. DECODING

Decoding (changing from digital to any other form) is the reverse of encoding and can often use the same circuits. The two main classes of decoding are.

(a) digital-to-digital
(b) digital-to-analog

Digital-to-digital decoding presents the same problems as does encoding, namely:

(1) adjustment of pulse width and clock-time.
(2) adjustment of pulse magnitude, polarity, and shape.

If the digital output of a computer is used directly in electronic read-
Occasionally, digital information from the computer is sent out "as is,"
puts associated with the computer, usually no adjustment is necessary,
but when the digital output is to be sent to external equipment, such as
to radio data link, any, or all, of the adjustments may be necessary.
and it is up to the receiving equipment to perform its own encoding.

As an example of digital decoding, suppose the output is to be sent back over the same data link as was used in an earlier example. The computer clock time is 5.0 μsec. and the data link clock-time is 100 msec. The computer will load information into an output buffer storage register, and when this loading is complete, it will be ready to be transmitted out at the 10-msec. rate. However, the output unit will need a timing pulse generator running at the 10-msec. rate to effect this transfer at the 10-msec. rate.

As an example of digital-to-analog conversion (often called "digilog") we may again use the ladder converter of Fig. 10-5. If this circuit is to be used for output scaling, additional circuitry must be added as shown in Fig. 10–6.

When some digital code to be converted is inserted directly into register F1–F4, this immediately defines the states of switches S1–S4 and immediately presents a scaled, precision current from the precision

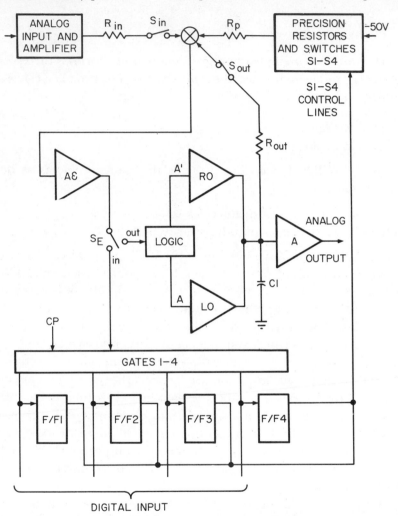

Fig. 10–6. Simplified ladder andacon digilog.

resistor bank through the summing resistor R_p to the comparison point. The computer control circuits are "calling" for a digital-to-analog conversion and not an analog-to-digital conversion, hence S_{in} is opened, S_{out} is closed, and S_e is switched to position "out." The negative precision current at the comparison point by itself causes the error amplifier A_E to have a false output that is coupled through logic (not shown) to power gate amplifier RO. This sets RO into conduction while LO is cut off, and the results of RO's condition is an increase in the charge stored in C_1. This rising charge, and associated rising current, is felt at the comparison point through R_{out}. The process continues until the output current is equal to the precision current. Since the charge on C_L is rising toward the negative voltage from A_E it will usually swing past the point where the current from RO equals the current from the precision resistors. When this happens, the error amplifier (A_e) momentarily yields a true output gating LO into conduction. The operating point of LO is set so that an increase in its plate current will draw current from C_1, lowering its charge. The output loop will quickly settle down about a mean voltage. The voltage stored in C_1 is isolated from the digilog circuit by an output amplifier (A). The analog output of this isolating-scaling amplifier represents the binary number stored in F1–F4.

C. OTHER CONVERSION METHODS

Straightforward digital-to-analog conversion can be accomplished across voltage-divider banks controlled by logic switching. An example is shown in Fig. 10–7. The logic switches are set according to the binary

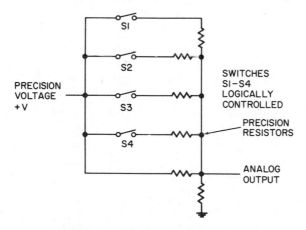

Fig. 10–7. Simplified digilog ladder circuit.

code of the number to be converted. This instantly changes the voltage dropped in the divider circuit, providing an analog voltage equivalent to the binary number being converted. In most computers, the "switches" shown in Fig. 10–7 are actually transistors that will be saturated (closed) by a true voltage and cut-off (opened) by a false voltage. When a transistor is saturated, it supplies a constant current into the ladder of resistors, altering the output voltage. If a digital output of 10 bits controlled 10 different transistors in a digilog circuit, there would be available $2^{10} = 1024$ different analog voltage steps out of this circuit.

10–3 Conclusion

Points to remember:

(1) Converting inputs to the computer is called *encoding*. Encoding is either:

(a) digital-to-digital, or
(b) analog-to-digital.

Converting outputs from the computer is called *decoding*. Decoding is either:
(a) digital-to-digital, or
(b) digital-to-analog.

(2) General-purpose computers require extensive input-output units. It takes a great many input devices to keep the "fast" internal computer busy.

EXERCISES

1. What problems may occur when accepting incoming digital information for use in a given computer?
2. What determines the accuracy in rotating encoding devices?

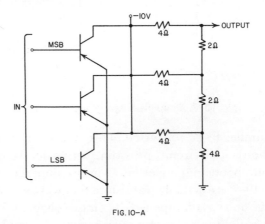

FIG. 10–A

3. Why is it possible to see more input/output equipment associated with a given computer than anything else?

4. In a 2 μsec clock rate system, how fast could a ladder andicon circuit produce a 13 bit output.

5. When would decoding be simply digital-to-digital?

6. A (large)(small) number of switches are necessary for very accurate decoding when using a ladder circuit.

7. With a binary input of 100, what is the output of the simplified digilog circuit shown in Fig. 10–A ($-5V = True, 0V = False$)

8. What is the output with 101 input? What are the output limits? (Use Fig. 10–A)

11

CONTROL AND TIMING UNIT

11-1 Introduction

Controlling the many computer operations is essentially a problem of proper timing. Computer control might be considered as a series of "orders" or commands. That is, the control unit says when to add, when to encode, when to transfer data from one register to another, when to look in the "buffer" stores for new information, when to proceed to any next step. Another way to look at this problem is to realize that all the main units of a computer (input-output, memory, arithmetic, control, and timing) are logically gated together. Each unit's internal structure is also logically gated together. The computer is not allowed to randomly perform functions in each unit. Two units cannot be simultaneously trying to fill the output register; the arithmetic unit cannot be using the same registers simultaneously for performing addition and subtraction. Operations must proceed in order. Therefore, some commanding device or signal is placed at the connecting gates that exist between units and within units, and this commanding device opens and closes these gates in a predetermined order. The computer, consequently, performs its functions in a logical manner.

180

11-2 The Clock-Pulse

The basis for time in a computer is the clock-pulse. Since the computer is operating much faster than the outside world, a clock divided in seconds is hardly sufficient. It is generally desirable to have the computer operate as fast as possible. The decision as to how often the clock-pulses should occur depends on several factors, including:

(a) desired speed of operation.
(b) desired or required accuracy.
(c) operating circuits' frequency response.
(d) circuit "settling" time.

The faster the clock-rate, the higher the speed of operation and accuracy of calculations in a given time. However, a very fast clock-rate may exceed the operating circuits' frequency capabilities, and the circuits and associated connecting cables may not be able to "settle" between very fast clocks. Hence, the last two factors generally set the upper limit of clock-rate for a computer design attempting to use standard cables and solid-state devices.

Clock-pulses operate at the same magnitude as the rest of the system logic. If +10 V is true and −2 V false, the clock-pulses will vary between +10 V and −2 V. If approximately −5 V is true and 0 V false, clock-pulses vary between 0 and −5 V.

In many systems, the clock-pulse is produced by a free-running, crystal-controlled (frequency-stable) oscillator in conjunction with amplifying-shaping circuits. This is the usual technique where the main memory is a magnetic-core type (Fig. 11–1).

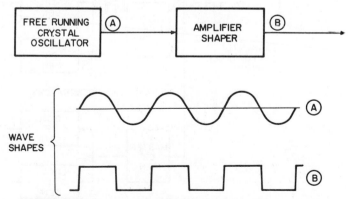

Fig. 11–1. Clock-pulse generator. Block diagram with associated waveforms.

When a system has a rotating-drum memory it is convenient to record a sine wave on one channel. This highly accurate, permanently recorded sine wave takes the place of a crystal oscillator and has the further advantage of keeping the whole system in step with the drum rotation. Should the drum slow down slightly, the clock-rate would slow proportionately and the system would not feel the difference. The same relationship holds true should the drum speed up slightly. With a drum memory, the clock-pulses are produced and distributed by the typical circuits shown in Fig. 11–2.

The driver reads the sine wave from the permanently recorded

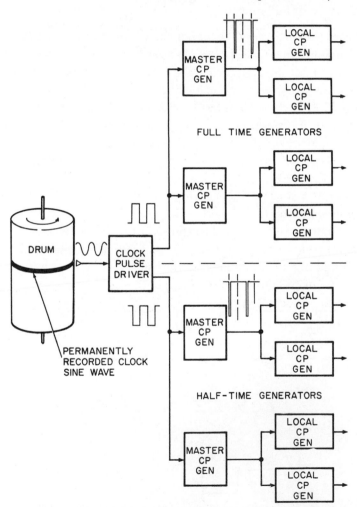

Fig. 11–2. Memory drum clock-pulse generation.

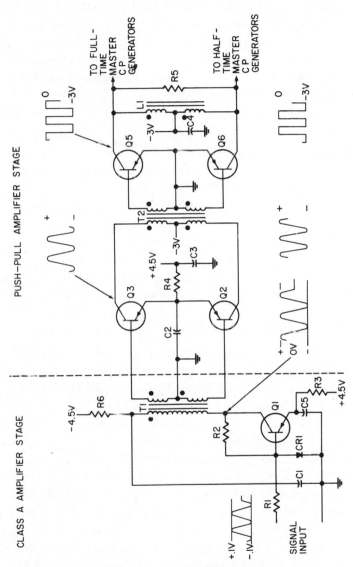

Fig. 11–3. Clock-pulse driver.

clock channel, shapes it in a Class A amplifier stage, then splits it in a push-pull amplifier stage, producing two outputs 180 degrees out of phase with each other. The square waves from the driver are sent to the master clock-pulse generators to be shaped into sharp, triggerlike clock-pulses. Since clock-pulses are used extensively throughout a system, many master generators are needed and even more local generators to supply the large clock-pulse load. Fig. 11–3 shows the clock-pulse driver circuit and waveshapes. Both outputs of the clock-pulse driver are utilized to drive two separate sets of master generators: the full-time master clock-pulse generators and the half-time master clock-pulse generators.

Inasmuch as the input circuits in the master generators are trig-gered only by a negative-going pulse, the clock-pulse outputs from the full-time generators compared with the half-time generators will occur 180 degrees out of phase with one another, but at the same frequency. This 180-degree phase lag, at the same frequency, is a requirement for proper operation of the write flip-flops. (See Chapter 8.) Figure 11–4 shows the master clock-pulse generator circuit and Fig. 11-5 shows the waveshapes of driver and master generator outputs. Local genera-tors have the same waveshapes as master generators and are needed to supply clock-pulse load in local areas Except for the output resistances, local clock-pulse generators and master generators are identical circuits.

The master clock-pulse generator (Fig. 11–4) consists of a blocking oscillator stage, Q1, with a shaping and buffer amplifier stage, Q2. The blocking oscillator is triggered by the negative-going edges of the square-wave input from the clock-pulse driver. The pulse width of the signal at Q1's collector is determined by the inductive action of T1 in conjunction with the discharge path of R2 and CR2. In the given circuit this pulse width will be approximately 0.3 μsec. Master clock-pulse generators feed local clock-pulse generators that are identical circuits except the output clocks are usually clamped to the logic level. A local clock-pulse generator is situated near the logical component requiring clock-pulses (i.e., flip-flops, etc). The clock-pulse generating circuits used in these examples will operate over a frequency range of approx-imately 200 to 400 kc where the clock-rate has been designed to be 333kc.

Since: time $= 1/$frequency,

$$T = \frac{1}{f}$$

$$T = \frac{1}{333}\, kc = \frac{1}{333} \times 10^3 \text{cps}$$

$$T = 0.003 \times 10^{-3} = 3 \times 10^{-6} \text{ sec}$$

$$T = 3 \ \mu\text{sec.}$$

Hence, time between clock-pulses (one bit time) is approximately 3 μsec.

These 0.3 μsec. pulses, 3 μsec. apart and varying between ground (0 V) and approximately -5 V, form the time-base, or clock, for a typical computer. These clock circuits are common examples of how clocks are produced when a drum is used as a main storage device. Computers using core memories have a separate oscillator to generate the basic

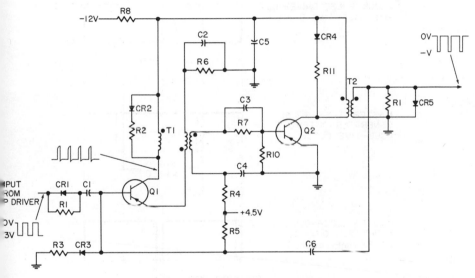

Fig. 11–4. Master clock-pulse generation.

clock-frequency sine wave. Also, a 3-μsec. clock rate is not necessarily the optimum for the whole computer field. Typical clock-rates vary from 1 μsec, for experimental computers to approximately 15 μsec. for some large general purpose computers.

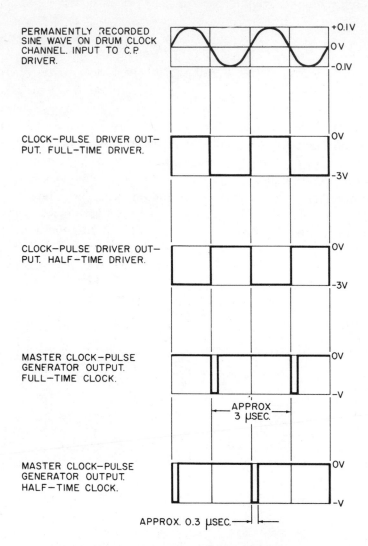

Fig. 11-5. Waveforms of clock generator system.

11-3 Counting Techniques

The time between clock-pulses is defined as one bit time, and within this time one bit, or digit, is held. A word is a given number of bits that describes a certain action or holds a certain amount of information; the number of bits per word usually varies between one computer and another. It is necessary to know when one word ends and another begins and even when parts of a word (format) occur. The method for determining these "time breakdowns" is to use counters. The counter is much like an alarm clock. At the end of a certain desired time, the counter produces an output pulse or "rings."

One example is the *ring counter*. This counter consists of a number of standard flip-flops connected to a common source of excitation (local CP generator). A four flip-flop ring counter is shown in Fig. 11–6. If the flip-flops are initially all reset, then a 0 exists at the S inputs of each stage. At any given time, a true pulse can occur at F1 (start pulse),

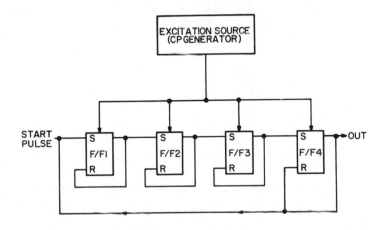

Fig. 11–6. Ring counter, block diagram.

and when this pulse AND a clock-pulse occur, F1 is set. The output of F1 does not appear until after the clock-pulse is gone and so F2 does not get set at this time. At the next clock-pulse, F2 is set and F1 resets itself. (Remember, the clock-pulses are gated with both the S and R inputs of a flip-flop.) At the next clock-pulse, F3 is set and F2 resets itself; at the next clock-pulse, F4 is set and F3 resets itself, *and* at this time there is an output pulse available. The original start pulse is not needed again since at the upcoming clock-pulse, the output of F4 AND this clock-pulse will set F1 and start the cycle over. Also, at this time the output disappears because F4 is reset. Every fourth clock-pulse time an output pulse appears, and if this counter happens to be used with a 5-μsec clock rate, then a pulse will be generated every 4×5 μsec = 20 μsec. A four flip-flop ring counter counts up four clock-pulses, a five flip-flop counter counts up five clock-pulses, etc.

A ring counter requires a flip-flop for each count, or can only count as many clock-pulses as there are flip-flops. Another common form of counter is the *binary counter*; it is so called because it counts in binary fashion. For instance, three logical variables may be represented in all their possible combinations by the truth table Fig. 11–7. The "high side"

	C	B	A	
LINE 1	0	0	0	BINARY COUNT = 0
2	0	0	1	1
3	0	1	0	2
4	0	1	1	3
5	1	0	0	4
6	1	0	1	5
7	1	1	0	6
LINE 8	1	1	1	BINARY COUNT = 7

Fig. 11–7. Total combinations of three variables.

output of a flip-flop could represent the variable A, another flip-flop B, another C, and if these three flip-flops combined could be caused to "progress" in such a manner that at CP1 their outputs were in the states of line 1 of the truth table, and at CP2 their outputs were in the states of line 2 of the table etc., then these three flip-flops would be counting binarily. The output of a flip-flop is, of course, dependent on what is happening, or has happened, at its inputs. It is desired to have the flip-flops behave according to the truth table, and this will be dependent on what is put *into* the flip-flops, so columns should be provided showing inputs (Fig. 11–8). This table shows a normal binary count proceeding with 000 at CP1, 001 at CP2, and finally starting over at the clock-pulse after CP8 or at CP1'. Now, what should the inputs to flip-flops A' B' and C be to produce this count?

    Examining line 1 at CP1, we notice that all flip-flops are in the reset state. Considering A first, we notice that at CP2, A should go into the set state. This can only be accomplished if a 1 is applied to the S (set) input of A at CP1. At CP3, A should go into the reset state, and, since at CP2 it is in the set state, this can only be accomplished if a 1 is applied to the R (reset) input of A at CP2. This cycle repeats itself for A from CP1 thru CP8. Notice that each time the flip-flop changes from

0 to 1, a 1 is posted in the S column in the line corresponding to the 0 state of the flip-flop when the flip-flop changes from 1 to 0, a 1 is posted in the R column in the line corresponding to the 1 state of the flip-flop. Using this rule, the inputs may be posted for flip-flops B and C.

	C	B	A	SA	RA	SB	RB	SC	RC
CP-1	0	0	0	I	0	0	0	0	0
CP-2	0	0	I	0	I	I	0	0	0
CP-3	0	I	0	I	0	0	0	0	0
CP-4	0	I	I	0	I	0	I	I	0
CP-5	I	0	0	I	0	0	0	0	0
CP-6	I	0	I	0	I	I	0	0	0
CP-7	I	I	0	I	0	0	0	0	0
CP-8	I	I	I	0	I	0	I	0	I
CP-1'	0	0	0						

Fig. 11-8. Truth table showing flip-flop inputs.

11-4 Input Equations

Where 1's appear in the input columns, write AND term from columns A, B, and C.

Inputs to:

$$S_A = A'B'C' + A'BC' + A'B'C + A'BC \qquad \text{flip-flop A}$$

$$R_A = AB'C + ABC' + AB'C + ABC$$

$$S_B = AB'C' + AB'C \qquad \text{flip-flop B}$$

$$R_B = ABC' + ABC$$

$$S_C = ABC' \qquad \text{flip-flop C}$$

$$R_C = ABC$$

The counter could be mechanized from these equations as they stand, but the flip-flop A and flip-flop B equations can be simplified.

$$S_A = A'C'(B'+B) + A'C(B'+B); \qquad B'+B = T = 1$$

Then $S_A = A'C' + A'C = A'(C'+C)$

Hence $S_A = A'$

$$R_A = AC'(B'+B) + AC(B'+B)$$

$$R_A = AC' + AC = A(C'+C)$$

$$R_A = A$$

$$S_B = AB'(C'+C)$$

$$S_B = AB'$$

$$R_B = AB(C'+C)$$

$$R_B = AB$$

The final input equations appear as:

$$S_A = A', \qquad S_B = AB', \qquad S_C = ABC'$$

$$R_A = A, \qquad R_B = AB, \qquad R_C = ABC$$

11–5 Mechanizing the Counter

Three flip-flops, A, B, and C, will have their inputs gated as dictated by the input equations (Fig. 11–9). Notice that this counter "runs upon itself." That is, no external input is needed except clock-pulses (not shown) that are applied to all flip-flops. Any "count" may be extracted by proper output logic. For instance, the AND gate shown extracts count three because count three is 011 and this configuration of the flip-flops is the only time the output of the gate will be true. There might be an output logic gate for any desired count or all counts.

The binary counter provides 2^n counts, where n is the number of flip-flops used. Had the previous example been a ring counter it would have required eight flip-flops to provide the same "count" capacity. However, the ring counter requires much less logic gating. By the same process outlined in the binary-counter example, any number of flip-flops may be gated together to count in any desired fashion. For instance, a particular application might call for a counter that counts 1, 3, 5, 7, 1, 3, etc. A truth table, laid out with this count, would yield the necessary input equations to mechanize this counter. In fact, there are several counters in popular use today, such as the Grey Code Counter, that do not progress through a straight binary count. That is, they do not count consecutively 1,2,3,4, etc. These counters have certain advantages in simplified logic, and for control purposes it is of no consequence in what

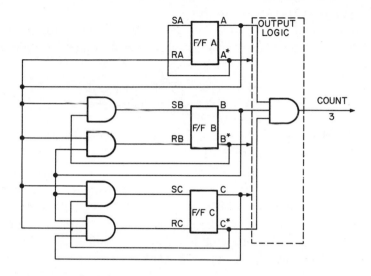

Fig. 11-9. Binary counter, logic diagram.

order a count progresses. Although these special counters have taken individual names, they are a type of binary counter since they are implemented by the same logic rules as used in the preceding example.

This example is typical of the type of logic that will actually be encountered in computers. That is, most logic is, in reality, "input logic." A computer is built of flip-flops, inverters, and boosters. The logic tells what should be put "in" these elements to cause them to behave in a desired manner. The truth table indicates what these desired manners of behaviour are. Notice that for the binary counter the sources of variables A, B, and C are flip-flops A, B, and C. Therefore the columns A, B, and C represent the "high side" outputs of flip-flops A, B, and C. There could be another table next to this one for the "low side" outputs A', B', and C', but this table is not needed because it would simply be in the opposite states in all cases. When line 7 of the table was selected as one of the AND terms for the necessary input to the set side of flip-flop A (S_A, why was the AND term written $A'BC$ and not ABC? The "1" notation in the S_A column indicates that a "true" voltage must be applied to the set side of flip-flop A at this time to have the flip-flop be set at the next time. This true voltage will be gotten from the AND term of line 7 where the "high side" of flip-flop C is currently true, the high side of flip-flop B is currently true, but the high side of flip-flop A is currently false (0). Hence, the low side of flip-flop A (A') must be selected to make this AND term true.

In most computers, a logic term will describe as many things about an element as possible. For example, typical computer logic would appear as:

$$AF06J = AF05* AF04 \ IF01 + IP02$$
$$AF06K = AF05 \ AF02 \ IF01* + IN02$$

where J and K define the two inputs to flip-flop (F) number six in the Arithmetic Unit (A); AF05 is the "low" or "reset" output of flip-flop five of the Arithmetic Unit, AF04 is the "high" or "set" output of flip-flop fours IF01 is the high output of flip-flop one in the Input Unit. and the whole term is ORed with the output of Booster (P) number two in the Input Unit. The K input has similar terms as inputs and the whole term is ORed with the output of Inverter (N) number two of the Input Unit. Flip-flop six cannot be set until AF05 is reset, AND AF04 is set, AND IF04 is set at the same time, OR any time IP02 goes true. The same reasoning applies to resetting AF06 (K input). This is the normal method for writing logic.

11–6 Control with Counters

One word of data for a given computer might be 26 bits. One bit time might be 3 μsec, hence one word for this data-processing computer is 26×3 μsec. long, or 78 μsec. The smooth, controlled flow of information and operations throughout a computer must take place bit-by-bit, either in parallel or in series.

If it were desired to transfer a 26-bit word from the main drum memory to some temporary storage register, and if this transfer were to take place serially, it would take one word time, or 78 μsec. But how can the computer know when the desired word is available, or when transfer of a word is complete? To solve this and similar timing problems it is necessary to count the bits in a word and generate a signal at the end of every 26 bits. This could be accomplished by any one of the previously discussed counters. It may be further desirable to count every word time. That is, after 26 bits, the counter indicates "count one," after

52 bits "count two," etc. In this manner of "building" the individual bit times into discrete "blocks" of time, computer operations can be orderly channeled (Fig. 11–10B). For instance, suppose a computer

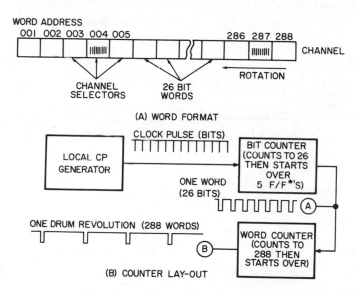

Fig. 11–10. Sample of control with counters.

drum memory can hold 288 26-bit words around one drum channel. If this channel were laid out flat, it would appear as shown in Fig. 11–10A, with each word entered under indicated addresses.

Remember, the 26 bits of word are arranged by the "word format." A group of timing elements might be connected as shown in Fig. 11–10B. Suppose every fifth sector (or word) of the illustrated channel were loaded with height information on airborne targets. Assume that at every other revolution of the drum every fifth word (height word) must be compared to see whether any are the same. The comparison circuit might be "controlled" as shown in Fig. 11–11. In this figure, the comparison unit is loaded with every fifth word during the drum revolution that the start/stop comparison flip-flop (RS type) is true. The comparison unit performs comparisons during the next revolution when the start/stop comparison flip-flop is false. Notice that no information can pass loading gate C except when the start/stop comparison flip-flop is true AND when the fifth word flip-flop (RS type) is true. The fifth word flip-flop is "set" (true) when the special counter counts up five words from the bit counter, A' and is "reset" (false) at the end of one word time (78 μsec) by the delay line output into the R side.

Many other forms of timing control are available in most computers. Where drum memories are used, it is common practice to have one channel with a bit recorded at "time zero" or "word zero," called an *index pulse,* used to synchronize the start of many counters and logic

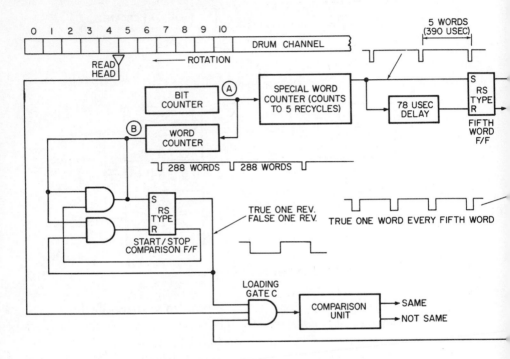

Fig. 11-11. Fifth-word comparison control.

gates. Since the rotation time of the drum represents some known value of time, it would be possible to record bits at certain discrete intervals, and hence alleviate the necessity of counters for frequently used time bases.

So far we have discussed control by actions occurring at known intervals of time. As seen in the previous example, the comparison of fifth words was made continuously, every other revolution of the drum. No provision was made to start or stop this continuous comparison cycle. Many control actions in a computer will be operating in this continuous mode. That is, for the previous example, it might have been desirable to have this comparison continue as long as the computer was running without any need for a start/stop provision. However, many control functions might be needed only on occasion, and some provision for initiating the control operation, and, in turn, stopping the operation upon completion would be necessary.

11-7 Programming

In general-purpose computers the method for starting, performing, and stopping any control at any time is called *programming*. A general-purpose computer might be *capable* of adding, subtracting, multiplying, dividing, extracting roots, solving trigonometric functions, and many other operations. The fact that the machine is capable of performing these functions in its arithmetic unit does not mean that it will automatically do them. It must be ordered to do them and it must be ordered to do them in the right sequence.

When a program (a group of orders) is being prepared, the programmer has a list of the machine's capabilities. These capabilities are often called "instructions." For example, a small list of instructions for a general-purpose computer might read as shown in Fig. 11–12. Instruction plus address forms a *command word*. The comment explains the command word.

COMMAND WORD		
INSTRUCTION	ADDRESS	COMMENT
01	XX	M ⟶ AG
02	XX	M ⟶ AG
03	XX	ADD AD TO AG

Fig. 11–12. Sample computer instructions.

Instruction 01 says: from the main memory (M), transfer (⟶) the contents of the word located at address XX to the addend register (Ad) in the arithmetic unit.

Instruction 02 says: from the main memory, transfer the contents of address XX to the augend (Ag) register of the arithmetic unit.

Instruction 03 says: Add the contents of addend register to the contents of augend register. No address is needed for this instruction.

For large computers, capable of many operations, the list of instructions is, of course, very long. It is important to note that these instructions are the machine's capabilities. That is, these are the things the machine can do. These instructions are "wired in" permanently as part of the machine's circuitry. If, then, the programmer wanted to add the data stored at address 23 in the main memory to those stored at address 17, he would, using the small list of instructions previously illustrated, write a program of "command words" as follows:

Step 1   0123   —meaning transfer from M the contents of address 23 to register Ad.

Step 2   0217   —meaning transfer from M the contents of address 17 to register Ag.

Step 3   03XX —meaning Add Ad to Ag.

There would need to be further steps (command words) to provide for transferring the sum (Ad + Ag) to some memory location or perhaps to an output register, but this requires more instructions than were included in the example. These further instructions would be available in a real computer.

The method, then, of orderly control of a general-purpose computer is to take the list of "instructions" for the machine and to arrange the instructions in steps (program) that solve the problem at hand. Next, the program (steps) must be loaded into its own store (program store) or into a reserved section of the main store. This would be accomplished with whatever type of input equipment is available. There may be room for several complete programs in the program store,and when the computer has completed the steps of one program it will move to the program store and begin following the instructions indicated by the steps of the program.

Figure 11–13 shows the sequence of general-purpose computer control. The programmer analyzes the problem and uses the list of instructions to write a step-by-step program, which is then entered into the program store. The control decoding logic starts through the program steps taken from the program store and, as each step is decoded, one of the "command word" lines is activated, opening certain gates and allowing the computer to perform the instruction (which might be add, transfer, multiply, etc.).

The programmer is the human operator of a digital computer. There are, however, several classes of people involved in programming. The person who enters program steps into the computer must be trained on the computer instructions (capabilities) and would handle simple or routine problems (pay rolls, data reduction, etc.). However, it takes a mathematician to analyze a very difficult problem so that it can be written out into the program steps. Even with complete knowledge of the computer's capabilities, a lay person may have no idea which step to write first to solve a complex differential calculus equation. Further, the more complicated problems with several variables cannot be solved by

Fig. 11-13. Programming control sequence.

simple, consecutive program steps. Many "conditional" points must be crossed where the steps begin to branch out and the entire program begins to look like a tree starting at the bottom and working upward. For instance, at step 105 of a given program, an answer is expected to fall within certain limits. If it is less than the limits, the program may return to step 85 and repeat; if it is greater than the limits, the program may return to step 67 and cause a value at this point to be reduced; if it is within the limits, it may proceed to step 106. At any rate, there was a chance for three branches, and there may be branches within the three branches, and there may be branches within the branches that are within the branches, etc. It is the responsibility of the mathematician/programmer to determine these needed steps.

The special-purpose computer is used to repeatedly solve special problems. Therefore, its program, once written, is stored (or wired in) in advance, and no additional programming is necessary until some new special problem arises. For example, one special problem of a special-purpose computer may be to calculate a possible intercept path between a friendly and a hostile aircraft. An operator depresses a button marked "intercept," and the computer proceeds through program steps that are already wired into the machine. It is possible to wire in these steps in advance because it is known what steps an arithmetic unit must go through to calculate an intercept path. And since this is one of the special jobs of this special-purpose computer, it is more desirable to have the program permanently wired.

Regardless of the complexity of the program for either a general-purpose or a special-purpose computer, the basic process as shown in Fig. 11-13 is followed.

11-8 Conclusions

(A) *Control* is the process of operating a computer in an orderly manner.

(B) Orderly operation is accomplished with a program of "steps to be followed."

(C) Each "step of control" opens certain "logic gates" within the computer.

(D) The "logic gates" open only at discrete intervals of *time* as determined by counting the basic clock-pulse into timed intervals.

(E) A program is a list of steps written by a human operator.

(F) The program steps are based on the computer's capabilities (instructions) and tell the computer exactly how to proceed to solve a given problem.

EXERCISES

1. In a computer with a bit time of 15 μsec., the leading edge of each CP would occur every _____ μsec.

2. If a computer has no drum there must be an _____ to create the basic time rate.

3. How many flip-flops are needed to construct a binary counter that will count to 17?

4. Would it be possible to construct a binary counter that would count backward (i.e., from 7 to 0)?

5. How is programming entered into a special-purpose computer?

6. Half-clock-pulses, as used by most typical computers, are:
   (a) Half the amplitude of the normal clock-pulses.
   (b) The same frequency as the normal clock-pulses.
   (c) Twice the frequency of the normal clock-pulses.
   (d) Half the frequency of the normal clock-pulses.

7. Calculate the analog voltage at the output for the figure below.

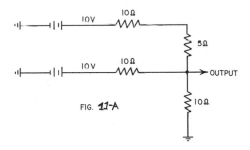

FIG. 11-A

8. Encoding means changing from _____ to _____
_____ with respect to a digital computer.

9. In most computers the local clock-pulse generators will be able to increase or decrease the clock frequency as needed at the local circuits.

10. A given digital computer operates off a basic 250 KC crystal controlled oscillator. The "bit time" for the computer would be:
    (a) 3 μsec.
    (b) 4 μsec.
    (c) 5 μsec.
    (d) 2.5 μsec.

11. Would the "logic" be less complicated to construct a 16 flip-flop ring counter or to construct a 10 flip-flop binary counter?

12. Needed: a flip-flop binary counter that will count 0, 1, 3, 2, 6, 4, 5, 7, 0 etc.
   (a) Draw the truth table.
   (b) Write the simplest logic equations for each flip-flop.
   (c) Implement the circuit.
   (d) Extract the count 4 on a single line.

12

MODEL GENERAL-PURPOSE COMPUTER

12-1 Introduction

Having discussed the necessary units, logic, and operations used for computer design, we shall now proceed to view these items as a whole by putting together a hypothetical computer. In this design, economy or efficiency is not our goal. We will put together the main computer units and cause them to solve some problem.

- Arithmetic Unit
- Memory Unit
- Input Unit
- Output Unit
- Program Unit
- Control and Timing Unit

Let us proceed, then, in the following manner:

1. *Analyze* the requirements of the given problem (or problems). That is, do we need to be able to divide, add, multiply, subtract, etc? This determines the computer's capabilities.
2. Logically *decide* what type of major units we need in order to solve

201

this problem. That is, what kind of arithmetic section do we need; what would make the best memory element; what type of input device(s) do we need; etc.?

3. *Mechanize* the computer. That is, having considered steps 1 and 2, let us link the chosen elements with some sort of control and timing circuits and then provide a program entry source.

NOTE: We are interested in how a general-purpose computer works when the units are integrated; therefore, we will solve only problems of of addition and subtraction. Greater arithmetic capabilities lend little to our understanding of computer operation, but do greatly extend the arithmetic section. We shall also limit ourselves to a word length of six bits and, hence, a maximum input decimal number of 2^n, where $n = 6$.

$$2^6 = 64 = \text{maximum imput number (decimal units)}$$

12-2 Analyzing the Problem

Given (hypothetically):

Problem A. $10 + 12 - 3 = X$.

Problem B. $e - f + g + h = m = X$.

Our only requirements are to add and subtract.

12-3 Logically Selecting Units

A. ARITHMETIC UNIT

A full-adder can be made to both add and subtract in a straight-forward manner. We will need a register to hold the addend and one to hold the augend. If our words are to be limited to six bits, then these two registers must be composed of at least six flip-flops each. Let us call the addend register "the upper accumulator" (Au) and the augend register "the lower accumulator" (Al). Let us say we want to perform calculations as rapidly as possible, so we should do our arithmetic operations in parallel. This means we will need six full-adders to handle all six of the bits in a word simultaneously. Further, we must provide a register to hold the answer from our adders. Call this the "answer accumulator" (Aa). Since we will be operating with binary numbers, the maximum number of bits in an answer derived from the addition of two six-bit terms would be:

$$111111 \quad \text{max. count (6 bits)}$$
$$+\,111111 \quad \text{max. count (6 bits)}$$

$$\text{carry} \quad 111110 \quad \text{max. sum} \quad \text{(7 bits)}$$

Therefore, our answer register will need to have seven flip-flops to hold the maximum possible sum. So far, we have the equipment shown in Fig. 12–1.

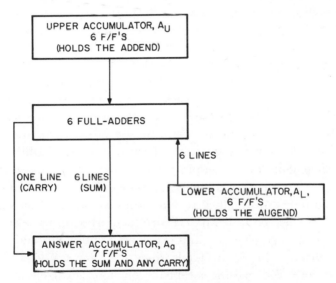

Fig. 12–1. Possible arithmetic unit.

With this much circuitry in the arithmetic section we could add two values and hold the maximum possible sum in the answer accumulator. Also, by providing some means of inverting (complementing) the number in either accumulator we could perform subtraction between two values. Inverter circuits in the six lines from either accumulator would accomplish this.

For most problems, we will probably have to add or subtract, more than two values; hence, we will need to "clear out" the answer accumulator and store the first addition (or subtraction) somewhere while we perform the second addition (or subtraction). Some sort of permanent memory is needed. Also, since most problems will have more than two values, it would be impractical for the adders to work on two values that were loaded into the upper and lower accumulators by slow input devices and then have to wait while two values were loaded in by the same slow input device. Some sort of input memory (store) is needed.

B. MEMORY UNIT

Considering the memory devices available, let us concentrate on cores, flip-flops, and drums. If we use flip-flops, we will need six for each term of any problem. We have not limited ourselves as to how many terms any problem may have, so this could mean an excessive number of flip-flops plus volatile storage. If we use cores, we will need six core-planes (corresponding to six-bit words) and, at least, four cores in the X and Y planes of each plane to have just 16 words of storage space. These sixteen word-spaces will have to be able to store all the terms in a problem, plus any first, second, third, etc., partial sums or differences obtained in the course of solving a problem. We could, of course, use a few more cores in each plane without too much extension of the memory or associated circuitry, but with cores we must provide clock-pulses from an outside oscillator plus extensive read/write circuitry control networks. A rotating drum will store more than sufficient words and is convenient for developing clock-pulses; however, it requires, outside driving power. For a small computer, such as we are considering, cores would be the most efficient and most economical. But, since later studies will involve both drum and core memories, let us select a drum as our main storage element, and use cores in other storage areas that may be needed. This is justifiable since we have set no limit on the number of problems we may want to solve consecutively and, hence, we may need a great deal of storage space for all the possible problem values. Also, by selecting a drum we can use previously discussed circuits to develop our clock-pulses, giving us a 3-μsec. clock rate with clock-pulses of 0.3-μsec. duration. Selecting this clock rate also allows us to use the previously discussed flip-flops, inverters, and boosters wherever needed.

C. INPUT UNIT

There are many input devices to choose from — punched tapes, magnetic tapes, punched cards, keyboards, and so on. With the exception of a simple keyboard, each requires extensive decoding circuits. We are not concerned with trying to keep our computer 100 per cent busy, so we should select the simplest input device: a keyboard. We can lay out the keyboard in any logical way to provide six key punches to correspond to the six-bit words of input data. In a further effort to simplify, we should let each of the six keys represent a binary bit, and then perform any needed decimal-to-binary conversions of input data on paper. The data input key layout might appear as shown in Fig. 12–2.

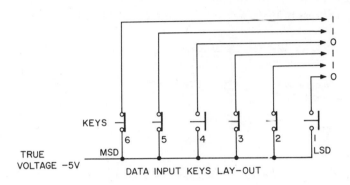

Fig. 12–2. Sample data input layout.

EXAMPLE:

Insert decimal number 54, which equals binary number 110110 (LSD on the right).
    Starting from right to left, do not punch the first button, punch the next two, do not punch the fourth button, punch the next two.

At this time the six output lines are set as shown—but notice, it took some time to set these lines. This physical time lag would hardly be tolerable were these lines to go directly to a drum for storage. It will be necessary, then, for these lines to set up an input flip-flop register (six flip-flops) which can be emptied into a drum in the proper time sequence (this would be an input buffer).

An address must also be indicated for any word loaded by these six "data input keys." We can lay out a number of buttons on our keyboard, excite them with logic level voltage (as was done for data input keys), and enter number addresses into an address flip-flop register (this would be an input address buffer). In an effort to have available as many addresses as possible and keep the buttons easy to "visually read," we could use the octal code. The address buttons might appear as shown in Fig. 12–3.

EXAMPLE:

Enter address 32.

set LSD buttons into 010 form
set MSD buttons into 011 form

That is (starting from right to left): Don't punch–punch–don't punch–punch–punch–don't punch.

Of course, the maximum address we can enter is 77. The outputs of these address buttons will set up the six flip-flop address buffer.

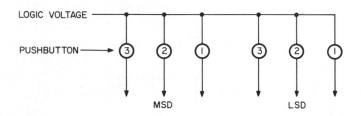

Fig. 12-3. Sample address input layout.

From our entry keyboard we can, so far, set up a six-bit input data buffer register and also a six-bit address buffer register (to determine the address at which the data will be stored). It will be necessary to add a "clear" button to our keyboard to reset these two registers between entries. It is also convenient to provide an "enter" button on the keyboard to "dump" the "input" and "address" registers into the store when we have finished loading them. For entering of data, we now seem to have enough buttons on our manual keyboard.

When the "data entry" and "address entry" keys are labeled, it would be practical to indicate their binary order. For example, the "data entry" keys would then appear as shown in Fig. 12-4. If the decimal number 23 is to be entered, the conversion to binary can take

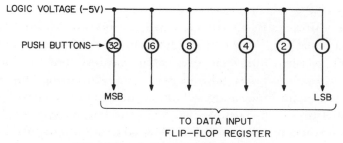

Fig. 12-4. Labeling data input buttons.

place at the keys by punching "16," "4," "2," and "1," which totals 23. It would be advantageous to label the actual coded "address entry" buttons using this same scheme.

D. OUTPUT UNIT

Now we have an arithmetic unit, a memory unit, and an input unit. We can provide a simple output by having the answer accumulator of the arithmetic unit light up a bank of lamps. The number that will be represented by this bank of lamps will be binary, but there will be only seven lamps and it is not too difficult to recognize the decimal value from a seven-digit binary number. For that matter, the decimal value corresponding to the light's order could be painted on the light bulb and read when the light is lit. More complicated, automatic output devices require digilog circuits, where the ensuing analog voltage would have to be calibrated to make sense. Generally, these analog voltages drive specific elements like scopes, typewriters, radio transmitters, nixie tubes, etc. We are chiefly interested in seeing whether we can properly implement the units we have previously selected to give a correct mathematical answer, so let us forego the extensive output equipment. We can start to piece together the units we have and see what form of programming control we might use with the assembled units.

12-4 Mechanizing the Computer

Figure 12–5 shows our proposed units assembled. To the right is the arithmetic section clustered around the six full-adders to perform parallel operations. Notice the use of inverters out of the lower accumulator (FA_{L_6}–FA_{L_1}) to perform subtraction by complementing. In the center of the diagram is the drum memory seen from a top view. One channel, not drawn to scale, is shown with recirculating registers around it. The inner line (of two lines drawn around the drum) is the "data into the drum" line. The outer line is the "data out of the drum" line. In the upper left corner of the diagram are the manual entry keyboard and associated input registers (buffer stores). Six "data input" buttons are shown at the top of the board with outputs to the data register. The octal-coded address buttons are at the bottom of the board. The rest of the circuitry shown comprises the control, timing, and programming equipment. This equipment will be discussed below.

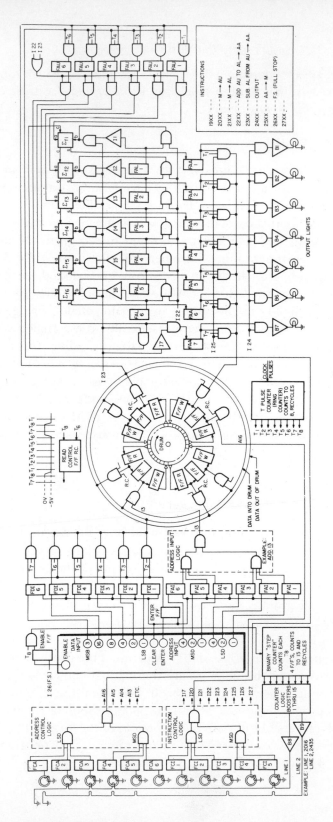

Fig. 12–5. Computer logic schematic.

A. DECODE LOGIC

First consider the logic elements within the dotted rectangles. All of these logic blocks (including the solid-lined "counter logic" block) are decoding networks. Just one example of many decoding gates needed is shown in each of the dotted rectangles. Let us analyze the "address input logic" rectangle.

When, for example, address 13 is to be entered by the address buttons, we want only one line to go true (or "hot") from the address register. Looking back into the outputs of the address register flip-flops FAI_1–FAI_6), we see that octal 13 causes the flip-flops (from top to bottom) to be alternately in the reset, reset, set, reset, set, set states. In order to take a "true state" line from this configuration, the AND gates would have to be connected as shown. There would have to be three more gates for some other address and three more gates for yet another address, etc. To draw out all the necessary decoding logic would take most of the diagram. This same type of decoding is employed in the other logic boxes. (If the AND gates were constructed to handle up to six inputs, one gate could provide the necessary decoding for a single address.)

Notice that the output from the data input register gates goes to the inner large circle around the drum to be entered into the main memory. The output from the answer accumulator (FA_{A_1}–FA_{A_7}) also returns to the inner large circle to be re-entered in the drum. Both of these outputs are entered serially. Remember that this circle is the data-into-the-drum line. Notice that the large outer circle (data-out-of-drum line) goes out to the loading gates for the upper accumulator. There would also be identical connections to the lower accumulator, but they are not repeated because of space limitations.

We need not show the clock-pulse circuits, as they can be the same as those already considered in earlier chapters. Assume clock-pulses are available wherever needed. We will take it for granted that we have available the necessary motor drive for our drum, the proper heads, read and write circuits, that adjustments have been made.

B. CONTROL AND TIMING

Considering control techniques, our first requirement will be some device that can signal each bit of a word or the start/stop of a word. It would be convenient to have some spare time at both ends of a word, and a pulse counter that counts to eight and recycles provides us with these requirements. The upper right corner of the diagram contains an eight flip-flop ring counter with an output line provided for each count, or "T" pulse.

Notice that throughout this discussion, to avoid confusion in lettering we will not use "T_0," although it would ordinarily be used.

In the lower left corner are the elements comprising our programming control. Remember, a computer has "wired in" a certain number of controls, or "instructions", it can perform, such as transfer, add, subtract, stop, etc. The program uses the wired-in instructions (complete capabilities) in certain laid-out steps to solve the given problem. Therefore, we need some wired instruction control logic (see diagram) and some way to indicate, timewise, when one step is done and the other is to begin. The "step counter" (which is essentially a "word counter") with its associated logic, shown in the lower left corner, provides us with the necessary "step timing" by advancing its count each time "T" pulse eight occurs. This assumes, at the moment, that each step of a program can be performed in one word time, i.e. step 1 of a program lasts from T1 to T8, step 3 lasts from T1' to T8', etc. Since there may be quite a few steps in a program, a binary-type counter provides us with ample counts without using too many flip-flops (as a ring counter would).

Now, the programming is a process of considering the computer-provided instructions (shown in the box at top of diagram) and the given problem. These instructions are arbitrarily selected and could be more extensive or even take a different form. The more "instructions" a computer can perform the more "instruction control logic" is needed. We can now write out program steps and store these in the main memory, or we can provide a special program store. In an effort to introduce several techniques, a type of program store is indicated at the bottom of the diagram. The programming registers FCI_5–FCI_1 and FCA_6–FCA_1 are "set" by inputs taken across the secondaries of small cores. The manner in which the primaries of these cores are wound depends on the program. For instance, suppose the first step in the program is to transfer some data from the main memory (M) to the upper accumulator. This action is indicated by instruction 20 XX. We would know which data we wish to transfer to Au and we would know at which address we had stored the data earlier. If it had been stored at address 13, the first program step would be 20 13, which says, "transfer to Au the contents of drum (M) at address 13." Since this is step one, it corresponds to the first count out of the "step counter," and the counter logic sets "line one" true. We want the programming register (FCI_1–FCI_5 and FCA_1–FCA_6) to indicate 20 13 out of the logic at this step one. Therefore, we will string "line one," from left to right, through the first core, not through the next core, not through the next, not through the next, and not through the next (completing the instruction part of program step one); then not through the next, not through the next, through the next, not through the next, through the next, and through the last core. When "line one" is hot, which it is at step one of any program, it will set the program register as indicated (20 13) because we have strung line one through the cores as indicated. We can proceed to string each succeeding line through similar cores in any way we want the program steps to proceed. This can, of course, be done well in advance. In fact, this is the advantage of using a separate store (other than the main) for the program. These small cores, or something like them, will be provided on a board with a sixteen-pin connector to be hooked to the "counter logic" booster outputs and an eleven-pin connector to be attached to the program buffer register. The "core board" could have been set up into a given program days in advance.

We may now proceed to attempt to solve Problem A $(10+12-3=$?) and see whether we have considered all the elements that will be needed.

12-5 Loading

Using the input keyboard, insert the problem values. To enter number 10, data buttons 8 and 2 must be pushed. This sets FIC_2 and FDI_4. The rest of the FD flip-flops should be reset; hence, we realize that the "clear" button should be pressed before the entry of any data in case any flip-flops were set at an earlier time. We must select an address in which to enter the number 10, and if we select address 13 we will be using the drawn-in logic on the diagram. We would punch "1" of the MSD buttons and "2 and 1" of the LSD buttons. This sets up FAI_6–FAI_1 as shown. The datum (plus adress) is now ready to be entered. Notice that the single "hot" address line from the "address input logic" selects a single recirculating register around the drum. This recirculating (drum) register might even be called "drum register 13" since only data at address 13 can get into this register. Data, which are fed to the inner large circle, attempt to enter every drum register. When the *enter* button on the input keyboard is punched, the "enter" flip-flop is set and the data are serially transferred from the data buffer register to the correct drum register by the timing pulses T2–T7. Let us assume the remaining problem values are entered as follows:

Data	Address
10	13
12	14
3	15

12–6 Program

Using the provided "instructions" the typical program steps for this problem would be:

Step 1	2013
Step 2	2114
Step 3	22XX
Step 4	2516
Step 5	2016
Step 6	2115
Step 7	23XX
Step 8	24XX
Step 9	26XX

Nine lines from the program counter logic would be threaded through nine core lines according to this program.

With this complete, the *enable* button on the input keyboard can be pressed, starting the program counter. The correct answer should appear at the output lights nine steps later, which would be:

$$T1–T8 = 8 \text{ bit times}$$

$$8 \text{ bit times} \times 3 \ \mu\text{sec./bit time} = 24 \ \mu\text{sec.}$$

$$24 \ \mu\text{sec./step} \times 9 \text{ steps} = 216 \ \mu\text{sec.}$$

Hence, 216 μsec. from "start" the answer appears.

If the functioning of those steps is carefully traced through the diagram it will be noticed that, in order to simplify, some necessary control logic is not shown. This may help us realize the number of logical considerations necessary in designing a real computer. The number of carefully simplified control logic features alone often tends to delay the final operational approval on a large, new computer for several years.

To maintain simplicity in this exemplary computer, notice the technique used to load a problem value into the upper accumulator. The loading technique is neither serial-shifting nor parallel but is "timed-serial loading." Data are taken from the common output line about the drum and applied to each input gate of the accumulator. Under the circumstances, the data would attempt to feed into every order of the adder section, but data are being extracted serially from the drum, and if we take note of the bit times at which the data are available, the correct time pulses may be applied to the gates to allow passage of only that bit of data that should pass that gate. From T1–T6, bits 1–6 from the drum are loaded into the accumulator. What determines which word, or address, is on the output line around the drum at these times? Nothing stops the T1–T6 pulses from repeatedly occurring at the gates. This is where the address portion of the "address control logic" output is used: at the output gate of the desired read flip-flop. If the lower accumulator is loaded by the same technique (using T1–T6 as control), how do data from the output line around the drum keep from going into the lower accumulator when they are supposed to be entering the upper accumulator? This is where the instruction portion from the "instruction control logic" applies, opening only the inputs to the upper accumulator.

These points may indicate the amount of thinking and consideration necessary to integrate the units of a computer.

12-7 Mechanization Techniques

In actual practice, the separate elements and circuits of this machine would be built as standard pieces. All flip-flops, inverters, boosters, read/write circuits, AND and OR gates would be constructed on miniature printed circuit boards, called "cards." Any flip-flop card would be interchangeable with any other of the same type (typically there are from two to six flip-flops on most recent computer cards). Hence, no flip-flop was specifically constructed and placed in a certain position to become, say, FDI_6 of the input data register.

Certain components, such as the drum and drive motor, would be easily recognizable, but the logic circuits in a computer all look the same. They are generally grouped, and sometimes color-coded, but should still remain interchangeable from unit to unit.

Consider also that in our sample general-purpose computer, no provisions have been made to show the necessary power supplies for logic voltages, circuit B+ and B−, etc.

To illustrate typical computer packaging, (Fig. 12–6) shows how this computer might look if it were actually constructed.

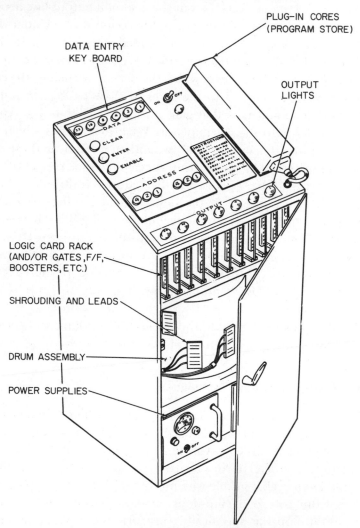

Fig. 12–6. Typical computer packaging.

EXERCISES

1. If a machine were built to solve only a given, simple problem, which would probably be larger: a digital or an analog computer?

2. Is a given general-purpose digital computer more complex than an analogous special-purpose digital computer?

3. For what period of time are the data stored in a digital computer's memory useful?

4. An analog computer is usually (faster) (slower) than a digital computer, and is also inherently (more accurate) (less accurate).

BIBLIOGRAPHY

Periodicals and papers

Motorola Integrated Circuits. Circular published by Motorola Semiconductor Products, Inc., Phoenix 8, Arizona.

Transistor Manual. Semiconductor Products Department, General Electric Company, Syracuse, N.Y., 6th ed., 1962.

Books

Phister, Montgomery Jr. *Logic Design of Digital Computers.* John Wiley & Sons, Inc., New York, 1958; 6th printing, 1961.

Richards, R. K. *Arithmetic Operations in Digital Computers.* D. Van Nostrand Co., Princeton, N.J., 1955, vols 1 and II.

McCracken D. D. *Digital Computer Programming.* John Wiley & Sons, Inc., New York, 1957.

INDEX